HE CHOSE CATHERINE

TRUST

HE
CHOSE
CATHERINE

"God hath chosen the weak things of
this world to confound the strong."

by SISTER MARY PAUL, O.S.F.

PAGEANT PRESS, INC.   *New York*

Published by Pageant Press, Inc.
101 Fifth Avenue, New York 3, New York

First Edition

Library of Congress Catalogue Card No.: 58-59576
Manufactured in the United States of America

NIHIL OBSTAT

✠ The Reverend Edmund J. Bradly
Censor Librorum

IMPRIMATUR

✠ James Francis Cardinal McIntyre
Archbishop of Los Angeles

September 30, 1958

To

"STELLA"

Mother of Many Daughters

Grateful acknowledgments are due to the Superior General, Mother Ignace, to her assistant Mother Clarissa and to my own Provincial Mother Macaria for their encouragement; to Mother Richard who drew the frontispiece and to Sister Monica who designed the book jacket. Special gratitude is given to my former Provincial, Mother Marita at whose request the book was written.

INTRODUCTION

In the course of centuries God has chosen divers instruments to fulfill a special task in this world. Catherine Daemen was such an instrument and never in her life did she want to be anything more than that. To God she gave full freedom to use her as He saw fit and thus she became that admirable woman of deep faith, implicit trust and ardent love for God and her neighbor. This peasant girl from a small village in the Netherlands became God's instrument in founding a Congregation of Sisters which has sent thousands of religious throughout the world on their mission of teaching and of works of charity.

It seems to us that in this book done in filial homage in the year that marks the hundredth anniversary of Catherine Daemen's pious death, Sister Mary Paul has portrayed the spirit of our beloved Foundress in a manner at once simple and inspiring.

Its appearance is timely in this our day when society and individuals are torn by doubt and perplexity, by fear and anxiety. May the quiet reading of these pages bring conviction and security, courage and peace through the realization of the fatherly Providence of God Who alone can still the restless heart of man.

M. IGNACE HOLTUS, O.S.F.
Mother General

The Generalate
Rome, Italy
Feast of Mary, Queen of the Universe, 1958

[7]

November winds prowled through the dark night, seizing the invading snowflakes and flinging them fiercely in all directions, but the angry howling passed unnoticed by the occupants of the Daemen cottage. It was quiet in there, quiet with that warm, peaceful hush that accompanies the arrival of love's dearest gift—a new life.

But, as the first rapture gave way to calmer thoughts, the mother was conscious of a little fear tugging at her heart. She put it from her and looked up to smile at her husband who had just returned to her bedside, and a gleam of alarm sprang to her eyes as she saw the worried expression on his face.

"Oh, Cornelius, you see it too! There is something wrong with our little girl, isn't there? Do you think she is going to die?"

Cornelius Daemen looked down at his little daughter. What did he, a man nearly forty years old and a father for the first time, know about babies? But the little one did look strange. It was not a good healthy red, which he had always heard was one of the distinguishing traits of the newborn. No, this little one was white, very white, with a bluish tinge, as if the tiny heart and lungs were finding the air of this earth too weak.

He spoke gently. "She does seem a little too small and pale, Trude, but that might not be serious. What does Mary think?"

At that moment, Mary, his sister who had been taking care of Gertrude, came bustling in.

"Now, now," she comforted in her assured, capable manner, "don't you two worry. I've seen them much worse than this." She fussed around doing the countless little acts that a kind heart always finds to do in a sickroom, but her thoughtful ministrations did not banish the fear from the hearts that should have held nothing but happiness.

Gertrude and Cornelius Daemen were middle-class farmers in the little village of Laek, in Limburg, Netherlands. They were both deeply religious and prayed that God would bless their marriage with many children. Cornelius was much older than his wife. He had been hoping that this first baby would be a boy who would grow into a strong, sturdy lad to help him on the farm; now this November 19, 1787 had brought him, not the longed-for boy but a girl, and evidently a weak, sickly girl at that! As is the way with fathers, however, one look at his own little girl fixed her in his heart forever and he would not have exchanged her for the most promising lad in the world!

The new parents were pathetically eager to rest content in Mary's superior wisdom but as the night passed and the morning approached the baby became noticeably weaker in her fight to adjust to this strange world.

"I think she should be taken to the church for her baptism before it is too late," said the anxious mother in the early afternoon.

Cornelius strode to the window, drew back the heavy shutter and gazed upon the wintry world outside. The wild night winds had ceased, and drifted high on field and road lay the snow, soft and beautiful; but overhead the skies were darkening again, and bending low as though straining to hold back the threatening storm.

"You know," he said, turning back to his wife, "it really

isn't an obligation to have the child baptized on the day of its birth. It is the custom and naturally we want to follow it, but we could very well wait until the weather clears or until the child is stronger."

"Suppose she doesn't get stronger, what then? Let it be done today, Cornelius. We do not want our little one to be even one day without the life of Grace. God will take care of her."

Women are strange creatures, thought Cornelius to himself. They pass from weakness to strength in the most surprising manner. He went into the kitchen where his sister, Mary Catherine and Gertrude's brother, Christian van Bree, were enjoying a plate of *balkenbrei*. He looked at them reflectively. Both were tired. They had been up all night and had worked hard through the day, Mary in the house, Christian in the barn and stable. It had been good of them to come to him in his hour of need and he hesitated to ask another favor of them. Mary rose to fix him a place at the table but he stayed her.

"Mary, Chris, we've decided that the baby should be baptized today, and in the church. Will you take her to Echt? I know I am asking a lot in this weather, but if it is too much for you, Mary, don't worry about it. Chris can take her in and I'm sure Mother Mayer or one of the other good women of the town will be glad to stand for the child."

That was enough for his sister! Let someone else be godmother to her only niece, and the little one to be called "Mary Catherine" after herself? No, indeed, not even the Ice King himself could keep her from taking the baby to Echt. She could take care of herself and the baby too, thank you! Such a wrapping and blanketing ensued that Chris laughingly declared that there was more chance of the child smothering than freezing.

No sooner were they out of sight than a hundred possibilities of accident flashed into the father's mind. What if they should drop the baby into a snowdrift, or suppose they veered off the road into one of the hidden ditches! Gertrude, though, was calm and undisturbed. Even when the afternoon winds grew sharper, and the sky dark and sullen, she did not lose her confidence.

"I am sure that all will be well," she told her husband when he wondered why they had not returned. "Remember that after the baptism Mary and Chris must take the little one to the altar of the Blessed Virgin and dedicate her to our Heavenly Mother. Then they'll stop at Mother Mayer's Coffee House for a little refreshment. God cares for our little daughter more than we do, my husband. He will take care of her. Let us trust Him."

Just as the evening Angelus was sounding from the little shrine of St. Anne, Mary Catherine was laid next to her mother's heart again. Anxious eyes could detect no ill effects; in fact, it seemed to both parents that her color was more natural, the breathing even and regular, and though the storm raged and howled outside, there was again only peace and happiness in the little cottage.

"You were right, Trude," Cornelius said happily, the next day. "The good Lord did take care of the child. How happy I am that we trusted Him. When she is old enough we will tell her of this experience so that she, too, will always have confidence in her Heavenly Father."

Little Catherine did not wait long for a playmate. By the time she was three another daughter had been born to Cornelius and Gertrude. Jenneke was a healthy, happy baby, much stronger than the still delicate Mary Catherine. Jenneke gurgled and laughed and dimpled at everyone and everything, and consequently, at once began to rule the little family. As they grew older the girls became inseparable. Trieneke, as Mary Catherine was affectionately called, was in danger of being a little too quiet and demure, a mite too serious, but with vivacious, impulsive Jenneke she just had to be gay, and sometimes a little mischievous! Different in temperament though they were, the sisters loved each other deeply, and in spite of Jenneke's penchant for gaiety, she never really enjoyed herself unless Trieneke was with her.

They did have such good times! The village of Laek, though very small, might have been a dull place to some people but not to the Daemen children and their friends. There were no high-priced, fashionable, specialty entertainments such as there were in the big cities, but the children knew nothing about them and so didn't miss them.

Early in the spring the hoop-rolling contests would begin. Girls and boys alike entered their hoops and for weeks ahead the cobbled street of the village was the scene of merry races.

Bikkelen, a form of jacks, was a very popular game, to say nothing of marbles, jump rope, hand-ball, and bowling.

Mary Catherine did not care much for sports and sometimes would refuse to join her sister and their playmates in a jolly race or game of ball. All that Jenneke had to do in such a case was appeal to their father who would say in his hearty voice, "Off with you, Trieneke! You're getting to be too much of a dreamer!" and the triumphant Jenneke would pull her along, much to the delight of the others who loved Catherine in spite of her quiet ways. She did not always approve of what they did, and would tell them in no uncertain terms, but she never carried tales.

The Dutch people have an almost passionate fondness for flowers and Mary Catherine and Jenneke were no exception. The gay tulips and hyacinths one naturally associates with Holland were not common in the southern province, but spring and summer were lavish with simple meadow flowers. Often the little Daemens would gather bouquets of violets, bachelor's-buttons and mayflowers, and later in the season, buttercups and daisies. Happily, they would carry their fragrant offerings to the beautiful rustic chapel of St. Anne in the village where they would arrange them before the statue of God's grand-mother.

Much as the two sisters enjoyed the companionship of their playmates, they were always just as happy by themselves around their own home. A favorite spot of theirs was a fork high up in the walnut tree from where they could look far out on the little world around them and wonder about it and the great, wide world which they would never see. They loved the cows, the pigs, the chickens, but most of all the cats. Though the special job of the latter was to keep the birds and mice out of the grain pit, they and their kittens were often pressed into service as dolls or babies for the little mistresses.

The evenings were the pleasantest part of the day, whether

in summer when they could sit outside, or in the winter grouped before the fireplace. Cornelius would mend his tools or sort his seeds; their mother spun or mended as the need might be. Sometimes the girls had a little handiwork also, but usually they just sat on their small stools listening delightedly to the fascinating stories of the saints their mother loved to tell. After a bit of storytelling their father would put down his work and sing some of the rousing songs of the country. He had a powerful, rich voice and the stirring tunes would send shivers of delight through his spellbound daughters. Night prayers would follow and off to bed the family would go, happy and contented with the world and their place in it.

Perhaps once a year, certainly not oftener, the family would go to the kermis at Maeseyck or Stevensweert. The kermis, or fair, had originally started as a church celebration, being held around a church that had just been consecrated. A Solemn High Mass had opened the festival, which was mainly of a religious character. By Catherine's time, however, the festival had become almost entirely dissociated from the church, the name only—kermis—a derivation of "Church Mass," and the opening High Mass on the anniversary of the consecration being all that remained of religious significance.

By early morning on one of these great days, the Daemens would be well on their way; Cornelius smart in his dark blue suit with the shining buttons, and his womenfolk resplendent in gay aprons, crisp muslin caps and their wooden shoes, or *klompen*, scoured to a brilliant white.

The Mass came first with this staunch Catholic family, and then followed a day of blissful delight, at least for the children. There were Punch and Judy shows, dancing dogs, rides on the bedecked and prancing ponies, joyous Maypole dances and breathtaking surprises from the fishpond! There were so many

[15]

amusements that not even the most determined child could possibly take them all in on one day!

Gaily covered *kraams*, or booths, were piled high with lovely ribbons and dainty laces for caps, soft frilly kerchiefs, and lovely hand-painted *klompen* with gay designs; garnet brooches and rings were displayed on beds of silk or velvet. Bright colored balls, appealing dolls from faraway Paris, ivory *bikkelen* sets, and countless other items calculated to stir the pulse of any little country girl, were set out in tempting array. Sugared and cinnamoned waffles, tender *oliebollen*, sweet *mopjes* and freshly baked *poffertjes* lured with their warm, spicy scents.

Each girl had a little money acquired by careful hoarding for months. Such a little bit of money and so many ways in which to spend it! Buying became a sort of delicious agony; it was hard to decide just where the money would bring the best returns in satisfaction. Unconsciously, Trieneke was imbibing a fundamental Franciscan principle; the burden of wealth outweighs its value!

There were grand and exciting days—all the more so because they were so rare. By going-home time, even Jenneke was always too tired to protest overmuch. The day would end as it had begun, by a visit to the Blessed Sacrament. Then came the moment for which Trieneke had waited all day. From her mother she had a great love for the poor and unfortunate, and Trude had often told her that we can always find someone a little worse off than ourselves to whom we can do good. As the daughter of a poor farmer the little girl seldom had the opportunity to bestow an alms, but at kermis her little store of money was hers to do with as she pleased. No matter what the inducements had been during the day she always managed to save a coin or two, and as they came down the big stone steps of the church she would drop these into the hands of one of the numerous beggars, giving along with them her loveliest smile. The poor fellow's "God bless *you kindje*" was sweeter to her than all the music of the kermis.

Besides the religious and family festivals of Saint Nicholas, Christmas and the Three Kings, the winter days brought other, if lesser, pleasures. One which they enjoyed very much was ice-skating. The river Maas did not freeze long enough nor hard enough to be used for winter sport but that did not keep the people off their skates! Some of the fields were considerably lower than the surrounding ones and were separated from them by dikes. These fields were completely flooded and when solidly frozen formed an excellent skating rink for the season.

But much as butterfly Jenneke would have liked it, life was not all frolics and outings. Far from it, indeed. Whenever possible the girls had to attend the school in Echt. Since there was no compulsory education law at that time there was but a minimum of school attendance and parents were permitted to keep the children at home whenever they chose to do so. Mary Catherine, though, loved school and managed to attend regularly enough to learn to read, write, and cipher very well.

One of the greatest attractions for her in Echt was the church of her baptism. Every day after school she would go to visit Our Lord in the dim, lovely, medieval church. A deep spirit of contemplation grew within her as she grew older, and though she did not realize what it was, she did know that she was happier in the church than anywhere else. Before leaving the church she would stop in Our Lady's Chapel. It was there, before the statue of Our Lady of Echt, that she had been laid as a baby fresh from the waters of baptism. Looking up to the beautiful face of Mary, Trieneke would renew the act of consecration that her uncle and aunt had made for her that day.

All Dutch children, especially those of the poorer classes, take part in the household tasks. Jenneke, though younger, was much the stronger of the two so she took the place of the boy who never came, and helped her father with the outside

[17]

work. She could dig potatoes, set out cabbages, cover the grain pit with the old sacks and milk the cows as well as any boy.

At harvest time Trude and Mary Catherine would put on their big aprons, tie the traditional red bandanas around their heads and lend a hand in the field; but for the most part, their work was confined to the house and the attached chicken house. And there was more than enough to keep them busy. Under Trieneke's willing and capable little hands the copper pans shone like gold when she hung them on their hooks next to the fireplace; the dishes, dried to a polish and placed in their racks, were so straight and orderly that the little blue ships painted on them seemed to be sailing across a white china sea. Flagstones and doorsteps were as white as water, sand, and Trieneke could make them. Guided and directed by her mother, she became skillful at the loom. She liked best of all to cook and bake. Cornelius vowed that she made better *boeren mik* (bread so white and soft on the inside, so brown and crisp on the outside) than did her mother!

Sometimes they would make *balkenbrei*, a succulent meat pudding which was cut into thin slices and fried. Whenever this happened her mother would say, "This is what your Aunt Mary made for your father and me the day you were born."

What more fascinating subject is there to any of us, than to hear, no matter how often, the events great or small that heralded our entrance onto the stage of life? So it was that Mary Catherine never tired of hearing all that happened the day of her birth. Enthralled, she would listen as her mother told of the blizzard through which the devoted aunt and uncle had struggled, bearing the little Catherine to the church, of her dedication to Mary, and the joyful ringing of the Angelus bell as she was put safe and warm into her mother's arms.

"God was very happy, wasn't He, Mother, because you and Father sent your little one to the church for baptism," she would say. "That is why He did not let any harm come to me and I began right away to get stronger."

"*Ja, kindje,* so your father and I believe. God is good, and when we do what we know is pleasing to Him, He will always take care of us. Remember that, my child."

"I will," the solemn little girl would reply, her earnest face glowing. "I will remember and I will always trust Him."

And she always did!

Startled, Catherine sat up in bed! There, she heard it again—a knock—another! Not loud, but insistent.

A highwayman? A French soldier? Terrified, her hands sought and clung to her scapular desperately, as through her mind rushed various tales she had heard of these night marauders.

The knocking grew louder, more urgent. It did not sound like a rap of violence but one never knew. Trieneke was young and she was frightened. There was no help to be had from little Jenneke sleeping so soundly beside her. Still holding the scapular as an inarticulate prayer, Trieneke pulled aside the bed curtains. The kitchen, so warm and fragrant and loving in the daytime, appeared strange and unfriendly in the shafts of late summer moonlight that poured through the upper half of the double window. She could see the heavy drape that separated her parents' room from the kitchen where she and Jenneke slept in the big recessed bed. The knocking was louder now. Making a huge sign of the cross, the child swung her feet over the edge of the bed, and at that instant the drape was flung aside and her father came into the kitchen. With one hand he clumsily held up his long night robe and with the other he grasped the stout cudgel every farmer kept by him for emergencies. Over his shoulder, she glimpsed her mother's white face, ghastly in the cool, silver light.

Instinctively, Trude's eyes darted to the children's bed and with a motion of her hand she signaled Mary Catherine to close her curtains. The girl did so, and crouching on her bed she murmured over and over, "Don't let it be a bad man, God, and don't let it be a French soldier."

Cornelius had drawn the bar from the upper half of the door and as the shutters swung back he jumped to the side with his club upraised in both hands, ready to bring it down upon any brash head that might be thrust through the opening. However, it was no enemy that stood without, but Father Jan Heiligers, the assistant priest from Echt!

"Good God, man!" Trieneke heard her astonished father exclaim. "Come in, come in, Your Reverence. Trude, Trude, it's Father Heiligers!"

Mary Catherine trembled now with relief and excitement. A priest here—in the middle of the night! What did it mean? The voices were now too low for her to catch any of the words. It seemed a long time that they talked and now and again she could hear her mother's little cluck of sympathy and concern. Just when she was sure she could not stand the suspense any longer, the bed curtains were parted and her mother leaned over her.

"Are you awake yet, *kindje?*"

"Yes, Mother."

"You have been a very brave and good little girl," her mother whispered softly. "It is Father Heiligers who has come to us. He is going up to the loft to sleep now so do not be frightened if you hear any noise from there. I'll tell you all about it tomorrow. Go to sleep now," and her firm, kind hands pushed the child back onto the pillow and drew the curtains together.

A priest in one's very own house! Why, it was almost like having God Himself! With an ecstatic sigh, Trieneke snuggled down into bed, and as she felt Jenneke's warm little body she was conscious of a throb of pity for the small one who had slept when such wonderful things were happening!

It seemed to Mary Catherine, the next morning, that the work would never be finished, and well she knew that not until the cottage was spic and span would she hear the whole story of the night's adventure. As Gertrude put the breakfast on the table she had said, "Girls, Father Heiligers is asleep up in the loft so be as quiet as little mice this morning." Jenneke's big eyes grew even rounder, but she, too, knew when to bide the time, and so, despite the curiosity that fairly made their little heads reel, they bit their lips and hurried to their tasks with a right good will. Finally, when the beds were made, the dishes put away, the floor freshly sanded, the chickens fed, and the eggs gathered, came the moment for which they had waited.

The facts which Trude told the children that morning, in terms best suited to their understanding, were briefly these: the revolution which had broken out in France, when Catherine was but two years old, had soon spread into many parts of Europe and was still raging fiercely. Because the French armies had defeated the Austrians, all former Austrian territory had been annexed by France. Since Limburg, the province in which the Daemens lived, had been a part of the Austrian Netherlands, it, too, came under French rule. With the annexation came the French Army of occupation, and with the army all the godless ideas of the revolutionary leaders. Convents and monasteries were closed and the religious banished; churches were looted and damaged. Their own parish church at Echt had been robbed of most of its sacred vessels and rich vestments three years before.

Things had gone from bad to worse, until finally, in May of this year of 1797, all Limburg priests had been ordered to take the oath to support the French constitution. Those who refused were to suffer the same consequences as the valiant French clergy before them—deportation to a penal colony or death by Madame la Guillotine. Since the constitution had been drawn up by the enemies of the Faith it contained many articles inimical to the Catholic Church and consequently no priest could conscientiously support it. The Limburg priests steadfastly refused to take the oath, and the process of liquidation had begun. The churches were closed and the clergy forbidden to say Mass or administer the sacraments. The people of Ohe-en-Laek and the other villages comprising the parish of Echt were fortunate in not being too far from free territory, and it was possible for them to attend Sunday Mass at Susteren where the French had no control. However, the two priests of Echt, Dean Ghysen and Father Heiligers had no intention of abandoning their flock and they concealed themselves in the cellars of the castle of Verdynen where they had celebrated the Holy Sacrifice every day until now.

"Some one," the mother continued, "must have betrayed our priests and yesterday they were warned that they had been discovered. Poor old Dean Ghysen succeeded in getting across the border but Father Heiligers is going to stay and take a chance of being able to carry on his work. In the middle of the night he left the city and came here to us for refuge. He knew he could trust your father and me—and you."

Putting her knitting down and gazing at them seriously, she continued even more earnestly, "Children, the priest is risking his life for all of us. During the day he will hide and by night he will visit the sick and the old; he will baptize the babies, give the sacraments to the dying, and when it is possible, say Holy Mass. He will go from town to town and from village to village, disguised many times and in many ways, and always in danger. When it is his turn at Ohe-en-Laek he will stay with us. Would you want him to be caught? To be sent to the terrible prisons, or be tortured and killed?"

"Oh, no, Mother, no, no!" they cried in horror, jumping up from their stools and running to her, "Oh, no, Mother!"

"Well then," Trude spoke quietly as she looked into the earnest flushed faces, "never, never tell anyone that the priest is or ever has been here. And when I say don't tell anyone, I mean *anyone*—the neighbors, your playmates, soldiers, peddlers, friends or strangers, not even Aunt Mary and Uncle Chris. It is not that we do not trust people, but the only way to keep a secret is not to talk about it at all. Can you do this?"

"Yes, Mother," they both answered soberly. "We will never tell anyone."

And they never did. Many times in the five years that followed until the concordat of 1802 did Catherine awake to hear the soon to be familiar pattern of knocks by which the priest announced his identity. Sometimes he stayed two or three days in succession; again, he might not come for weeks or even months and then only for a few hours. Usually he arrived just before dawn broke and did not leave the cottage until night had lowered her friendly shades to shelter him. Thus neither Trieneke nor Jenneke had an opportunity of seeing him. Often and again they begged to be allowed to get up to welcome him, or to stay up and bid him God-speed, but the wise parents steadfastly refused, thinking, rightly, that the less the children knew about the matter, the less they could tell if the occasion should ever arise. Jenneke, realizing the hopelessness of the request, gave up, but the otherwise docile Mary Catherine returned to the attack again and again. At the most unexpected times and places she would bring it up. This determination, together with her undoubted level-headedness and staunch courage for the right, finally won her point, and thus it happened that shortly after her twelfth birthday she was told the good news. Father Heiligers was leaving that night and she might stay up until he had gone!

That cold, dark winter night marked a turning point in Catherine's life. As she sat listening enthralled to some of the priest's adventures, he turned to her suddenly and bent his intent gaze upon her.

"How old are you now, Catherine?" he questioned.

"Twelve, please, Father," Trieneke said shyly.

"Twelve, eh?" He leaned back in his chair and drew on his long pipe. "Twelve. Well it seems about time that—" He broke off with a twinkle in his eye. "Are you a good girl?"

Catherine faced him bravely though her lips quivered a little. He was a priest and one must always answer the priest so she said hesitatingly, "I try to be good, Your Reverence, but sometimes I'm stubborn, and my father says I spend too much time praying."

Cornelius grinned self-consciously as the priest looked at him quizzically. "It isn't exactly that she prays too much," he explained apologetically. "It's rather that she doesn't play enough."

The priest looked at her kindly. "That doesn't seem to be such a bad fault, Trieneke. But what about this stubbornness? Do you refuse to obey, or cry and sulk if you do not get your own way?"

Trude opened her mouth as if to speak but Father Heiligers silenced her and waited for the girl to answer.

"Oh, no, Father," she gasped, "but I-I pester."

"Oh, you do, eh? And what do you pester about, for instance?"

Unaccustomed tears shone in the girl's eyes as she explained. "To stay up to meet you, Father, and for permission to ask you—" here she glanced beseechingly at her mother who nodded encouragement—"to ask you if you would prepare me for my first Holy Communion."

And so it happened. Each time the priest came he spent a few of his precious minutes instructing Catherine for this wonderful event and so well did she cooperate that it was not long until he could say, "Now it is enough. You are ready."

One spring day, when the tulips and narcissi were sending out their fragrant message of sweeter joys to come, and the birds were trilling their praises of God, Mary Catherine received her dear Lord. Her heart carolled too. A song that she had never heard found a new birth in her soul that day.

"I have found Him Whom my soul loveth. I have found Him and I will not let Him go."

The years slipped by as years do, each one a little faster, and suddenly, or so it seemed to Trude and Cornelius, Catherine was a young woman! She was still a different one, this eldest child of theirs! Warmhearted, lovable, generous, but with a delicacy and reserve not found in the other village girls, not even in Jenneke. Affectionate and gay within the family circle, out of it she was shy, seeming never quite at ease in her surroundings. She differed in another way, too. Though a perfect housekeeper and a lover of children, she evinced no desire for a home of her own and gradually the young lads learned that Mary Catherine was definitely not interested.

Affairs were not going well with the Daemens. French taxes, like leeches, were draining the resources of rich and poor alike in Limburg. Year after year the farmers were practically stripped of their crops and the best of their livestock taken to feed Napoleon's hungry soldiers. Cornelius' little property was in a bad state and years of insufficient income made it impossible for him to make the necessary repairs and improvements.

Ever since Mary Catherine had realized the situation she had been urging that she be allowed to go to work as most girls of her class did, but Cornelius had steadfastly refused. He knew she was not strong enough for farm labor, and if she went into house service it would mean that she would have to live away from home. Only in a city would she find a position and Cornelius had the farmer's innate fear and hatred of city life. No girl of his was to be exposed to its dangers.

And so he struggled along from season to season, trying his best to keep his family from feeling the pinch of real poverty, but at last the time came when he was forced to admit defeat. Enough grain and vegetables had been salvaged to see them through the coming winter but there had been nothing left for marketing after the government agents had loaded the army wagons. Consequently, he had no money to purchase seed for the spring planting.

Mary Catherine renewed her petition. "Let me try it at least, Father. Even a small amount of money coming in regularly will help you to get on your feet again. You'll be able to get what you need for next season's crop and perhaps even replace some of the livestock. You have always taught us that God will provide and I believe it, but I think that He wants us to do what we can, ourselves."

Cornelius gave in, of course. What made it so hard for him was not only the blow to the natural pride that a man feels in caring for his own, but that he realized well that his daughter was making a tremendous sacrifice. The exceptionally deep love he had for his first-born gave him an understanding of her sensitive, shy nature. Mary Catherine understood him also, and knowing his reluctance was mainly on her account, she took care to let him see no trace of the dread she felt at leaving home. "Don't worry," she told him gaily. "Mother's praying that I get into a good home and she's so insistent about it that I'm sure the good God will find a place for me in the best Catholic family in Limburg."

God did better than that! One day Cornelius returned from Maeseyck where he had gone on business, bringing the astounding news that Mary Catherine was to go to work the following week in the household of the parish priest of

Maeseyck! This medieval town of Belgium was just across the river Maas, almost opposite Ohe-en-Laek. Often, on bright days, Catherine had looked over to the beautiful church spires in the distance and prayed as the sweet tones of the Angelus bell came clearly across the river. And now she was going to live in that historic city, in the shadow of the lovely church.

The day of departure came too quickly. Jenneke was torn between the excitement of having her sister work in the big city, and grief at losing her loved companion. Catherine herself, and Trude and Cornelius, with that reserve and stolidity common to most of their countrymen, were calm and dispassionate in their farewells. But each knew that the others' hearts were aching with the pain of separation and the knowledge that this event was a turning point—that never again would things be quite the same.

And so Catherine stepped out into the world.

*　*　*　*　*

Early morning sunbeams peeping over the tops of the tall poplar trees that fringed the road found Mary Catherine already more than halfway home. Nowhere does spring come lovelier than in Holland. The bright tile roofs and whitewashed walls of the small farmhouses she passed were fresh from their dewy bath. The hedges and budding orchards shimmered with the thousands of diamonds that the greedy sun had not yet stolen.

It was a good two hours' walk from Maeseyck to Laek but the time did not seem long for Catherine. She said her rosary, and when the highway was clear she sang her favorite hymns to the accompaniment of the joyous morning calls of the meadow larks. She loved these monthly visits to the little homestead. Three years had not dimmed the happiness she felt when on each occasion she put her wages into her mother's big pocket and saw the dear face light with loving gratitude.

exchanged. Mary Catherine heard with interest anything connected with her loved village and she in turn gave accounts from the city. Maeseyck was one of the stopovers for troops going to and from the front, and consequently a political hotbed. She had been present in the church the day the whole congregation got up and left when the priest started the requested prayer for Napoleon! Items like this, straight from the scene of action, were as so many feathers in the cap of Cornelius, who passed them on to his friends in the village with, "My daughter, Catherine saw. . . ."

When the little fund of present events was exhausted Cornelius would tell some enthralling bit from the checkered history of valiant little Holland, and sing one of his rousing songs in his still powerful baritone. With a glass of Trude's homemade wine and a dish of *koekjes* made just for Mary Catherine's visit, the homey comfortable evening would come to a close. Night prayers were said before the little statue of Our Mother, and off to bed they would go, happy with that peace that only the members of a closely-knit family enjoy.

And now Mary Catherine had to give up that dear time to go, of all places, to a dance! She did not frown on such amusements. She simply saw them as of no value in her scheme of life, and true to her singleness of purpose and straightforward character, she disregarded them.

Evening, dreaded by Trieneke and desired by Jenneke, came too quickly for the one and too slowly for the other. Arrayed in their finery, the girls presented themselves to their parents for approval. Jenneke's deep beauty was heightened by her colorful attire.

"How pretty she is," thought Trieneke fondly as Jenneke pirouetted around her admiring parents. "There is certainly no resemblance between us!"

Perfectly true, Mary Catherine was not pretty. She was not even good-looking. But her eyes were a lovely warm brown under delicate brows and short, thick lashes, and firmly moulded chin and lips did not detract from the sweetness of her expression. Cornelius, looking at her in her deep blue bodice, crimson apron and the tight fitting cap with its gay little wings, thought her beautiful.

Hurrying to the village square, the girls were met by a group of other young people going to the dance, and they were all driven together in a big farm wagon.

The evening was not as hard on Mary Catherine as she feared it was going to be. Many of her childhood friends were there, and genuinely glad, though somewhat surprised, to see her in a dance hall! Jenneke found her a place where she could see without being seen too much. There she was left alone for the most part, happy in her solitude. Occasionally some young fellow would ask her out, only to become embarrassed at her embarrassment in refusing him. Jenneke paid her a few breathless little visits, her face glowing with happiness and enjoyment.

Anxiously Mary Catherine watched her as she was claimed by this one or that, always the center of attraction, but soon even her inexperienced eye noted that Jenneke could take care of herself. Catherine noticed, too, that a certain blond young giant seemed to be getting the lion's share of her sister's attention. Jenneke had introduced him early in the evening as Steven Suilan from a neighboring village.

At last it was all over and they were on their way home. The obliging driver dropped each one of the merry group at her own house and in no time at all Mary Catherine and Jenneke were slipping out of their finery.

"Now, confess, Trieneke," said Jenneke softly, "that it was a lovely evening and not at all what you thought it was going to be. Thank you a thousand times for going with me. I had a wonderful time and you could have had the same, I am sure."

[33]

Catherine nodded. "I'm glad you enjoyed it, Jenneke. It was nice, but I assure you again that it is not what I want. I don't intend to lead a social life or get married, so why should I act as though I were? Such things are right for you, little sister, but for me—no."

For a few minutes there was silence, then shyly Jenneke asked, "What did you think of Steven?"

Mary Catherine smiled. "Well really, Jenneke, I just met him. I haven't had time to think about him! However," she continued as the girl's face fell, "he did seem like a fine young man. Do you like him?"

Jenneke dimpled and her eyes sparkled in the flickering candlelight, but she evaded the question with one of her own. "Do you think he likes me?"

Before Mary Catherine could reply, Jenneke blew out the candle and both girls fell on their knees beside the bed for their night prayer. Jenneke finished first and got into the big bed where she stretched gratefully under the cool sheets. By the time Mary Catherine joined her, Jenneke was nearly asleep but she roused herself to whisper, "Trieneke, I wish you would be more like the rest of us. It isn't as if you could be one of those nuns Mother tells us about. You know the French closed all the convents here and drove all the religious out. What *are* you going to do?"

"I *don't know*," was the dejected reply. "I don't know. I've thought about being a nun, but as you say, where could I find a convent in these days? And yet—oh, if I only knew what God wants of me, nothing would stop me from doing it!"

"Well, I know what I *hope* He wants of me," was Jenneke's last drowsy murmur. "And I'm going to do it too, I think—if somebody asks me!" And with a contented little sigh she dropped off to sleep, leaving Mary Catherine lying wide-eyed beside her.

F lushed, Mary Catherine turned from the fire as the kitchen door opened and a familiar voice called, "Catherine?" Before she could move, Jenneke had entered, taken the spoon out of her sister's hand, swung the crane from over the fire, and pushed her down upon a chair. "I shan't stay long, Trieneke," she said, perching herself upon the edge of the table, "and Their Reverences' stew will be none the worse for a little delay!"

"Oh, it's good to see you, Jenneke," and Mary Catherine's warm smile flashed at the pretty face above her. "You don't often come to Maeseyck to see me." She was amazed at the strained and anxious expression that came to her sister's face as Jenneke said slowly, "I wonder if you will say that in a few minutes, Mary Catherine?" Then suddenly, "Trieneke, you like your life here, don't you? You are happy here?" Surprised, Mary Catherine looked at her, Jenneke knew she liked it! Perplexed, she answered soberly, "Indeed, I love it. Perhaps it is not just what I hoped for, but I realize that it is the nearest I will ever get to religious life and I am very, very content. Why, little sister?"

Springing to her feet, the younger girl paced back and forth a few seconds before she answered abruptly, "Because I am going to get married in a few weeks!" and continued more quietly, "I know it will mean a big sacrifice for you,

[35]

Trieneke, but we just can't wait any longer. All the other girls are raising families and Steven's folks are encouraging him to marry another girl who will make a home for him. He won't do it, of course, because he loves me. But it isn't fair to him, or to me, either." Mary Catherine's face paled as she caught the import of Jenneke's words, but her clear eyes did not waver. "If only we could take Mother and Father to live with us—but his mother won't hear of it," Jenneke went on. "I hate to do this, but I can't give him up. I want my own home, Oh, Trieneke, what shall I do?" Mary Catherine put her arms around the sobbing girl and held her close. Later, she would fight her own battle, but now she must think only of her sister. Steadying her voice with an effort, she consoled her weeping sister.

"I'm sorry, too, Jenneke, sorry that I have been so blind to your sacrifice. You've been so fine about it that I just didn't understand how it was with you and Steven. Don't worry. I'll stay with Mother and Father."

After Jenneke had gone, Mary Catherine went about in a daze. Mechanically she went on with the work, but her mind was in a whirl as her thoughts went back over the past years. They had been such happy, fruitful ones, holding so much of both material and spiritual blessing. Shortly after her "first and last" appearance in society (the dance at which Jenneke and Steven had become interested in each other), the old housekeeper at the rectory had died and Father Borman had unhesitatingly put Mary Catherine in charge of his household. He knew well that her comparative youth for such a position was more than offset by her maturity of judgment. More, she possessed the crowning virtue of a priest's housekeeper—discretion. With her advancement came a substantial increase in salary, which, together with Jenneke's success on the little farm, had freed Cornelius and Trude from any fear of poverty. Often she was enabled to relieve the distress of the poor and sick both from her own purse and from the provisions of the generous pastor who gave her a free hand in this matter.

But the most valuable gift the years had brought was a spiritual one through the person of Father Christian Opt Endt. At the time of the expulsion of the religious from Maeseyck, Father Christian was one of the Capuchin friars in charge of the very church at which Father Borman was now the pastor. He had succeeded in evading detection and had secretly carried on his priestly work in the city. When the church was reopened with Father Borman as pastor, Father Christian was appointed as assistant. Mary Catherine, in common with the other people of her generation, had never seen a religious, and the poor brown habit, which Father Christian now wore openly, seemed a thing of beauty to her. This zealous priest was worthy of his garb, and through his daily contacts with Mary Catherine he recognized in this simple peasant girl a soul of sterling worth and great spiritual promise. Under his direction and guidance, Mary Catherine's inner life began to take shape and her hitherto rather vague desires crystallized into a definite form of action. He unfolded to her the beauties of the Franciscan way of life. It was the loving, humble, poor man of Assisi that captured her heart, which no other had ever caused to beat one degree faster.

As she had told Jenneke, she was quite happy. Her longing to be a nun seemed destined to unfulfillment, so she accepted, with cheerfulness, this substitute. And it was a life of service, first of all to the priests in her care, for whom she delighted to render all manner of little kindnesses far beyond duty's demand. Then, too, through her pastor's generosity and her own means, she was so often able to help the war stricken families with baskets of food, and her busy needle turned out many a warm garment for the poor little fatherless babies that war always leaves in its trail. Just a few doors away was the beautiful old church where every morning she assisted at the

Holy Sacrifice and very often met the dear Lord in Holy Communion. Never a day passed that she did not slip in for a few minutes with this Jesus, Who was slowly, but so strongly, drawing her to a more intimate union with Himself. And now this happy, useful, spiritually-rich life was to end! It just couldn't be true. Surely this was where God wanted her!

A thousand chaotic thoughts beat hard against her heart. She could not think coherently here in the kitchen, with all the dear, familiar, material things around her, and as soon as the little maidservant returned from the market, Mary Catherine slipped her shawl around her shoulders and hastened to the church. The lovely Renaissance altar gleamed like a jewel in the cool darkness, and the sanctuary lamp beckoned her forward. The struggle was sharp but brief, and soon peace returned and love and trust flooded her soul. "It's all right," she whispered to the Tabernacle. "If this is what Your Providence wants, it's all right."

*　　*　　*　　*　　*

At last it was over and Jenneke belonged to the tall earnest young man at her side. The civil service which the government demanded, had been attended to in the morning at the town hall, but it had meant nothing to this Catholic couple. It was the beautiful prayers of Holy Mother Church and the blessing of God's priest that made them man and wife. Mary Catherine felt the tears trembling beneath her eyelids but she forced them back and smiled lovingly on the pair as they passed her on the way out of church. "Bless them, dear Lord," she prayed again. "Keep them always as close to You as they are now." Jenneke was unwontedly pale, but her eyes held a wealth of joy and her smile radiated happiness as she received the greetings and wishes of her friends and relatives. The Dutch dearly love a wedding, and all who could possibly leave their work had done so. Both Jenneke and Steven were popular with the young folk and favorites of the older generation, and the square in front of the church was filled with young and old. It was just as well, Mary Catherine thought, that custom demanded the wedding feast to be held in the home of the bridegroom, for never, never, could the modest little Daemen cottage provide for all these people!

Hardly had she embraced her sister and pressed Steven's hands warmly when they were practically lifted up into the high bridal carriage by a merry group of the party. Mary Catherine would have liked to slip off with the older ones who hurried on to the Suilen farm for last minute preparations, but she, too, was caught and placed in the second carriage with Steven's brothers and sisters. In no time at all, the line of carriages and wagons was filled with laughing groups, and at a signal from Steven they started on the traditional bridal tour. Singing and merry-making to their hearts' content, they rode from one to another of the surrounding villages, stopping at every *raadhuis* for coffee and cakes. The merry jingle of the silver bells on the wedding carriage was a signal for shutters to be thrown open. Busy housewives stopped their work to watch and call their blessings on the blushing bride and groom. And the children! It didn't seem possible that so many children could assemble so quickly! Knowing their time-honored privilege, they seized the horses' bridles and clambered up the high steps of the carriage, chanting the same words that their parents and grandparents before them had used on such occasions, "Bride, Bride, strew your sugars about!" And from a seemingly inexhaustible supply of candies, Steven filled his wife's hands, and standing up on the carriage seat Jenneke literally "strewed" her sugars about! With shouts of glee the innocent pirates dashed off to collect their bounty, leaving the party to continue on its way until attacked by another marauding band. It was all glorious simple fun, and tired and happy they arrived at the Suilen farm late in the afternoon. Steven lifted Jenneke down and hand in hand they ran up the path.

All too soon the time came for the Daemens to leave. They did not stay for the dance that was to be held, but left early in the evening. Ohe-en-Laek was a good distance, and, too, the excitement had been a little too much for Cornelius, who was aging rapidly. "It's a good thing," he remarked with a chuckle, "that Trieneke here doesn't want to get married. I don't think I could go through this again!" Jenneke broke down completely when she said good-bye. Never before had she spent a night away from them and she grew a little hysterical until her father said gently, but firmly, "That's enough now, my girl, or we'll take you back home with us." That was enough to send her flying to her husband, and in the laughter that followed, the farewells were easily said and soon the little family of three was on its way homeward.

They drove along in silence; hearts were too full and bodies too tired for speech. Dusk was just beginning to fall and the first venturesome little stars were creeping out from behind the velvet curtain. All was quiet save the faint rustle of the leaves as the breezes kissed them goodnight, and the rhythmic *klop-klop* of the mare's hooves on the hard earth road. Mary Catherine sensed rather than heard that Trude was crying softly, mother-tears for the loss of her youngest. Cornelius must have felt it too, because he reached over and rested his old gnarled hand on Catherine's, as he said gently, "We've got our Trieneke, Mother."

Spring had come again to Ohe-en-Laek. The clean, pungent odor of newly-tilled earth filled the air; cowbells jingled gaily and in the budding trees birds warbled and chirped busily as they built their cozy nests. One could almost hear the violets and crocuses pushing their eager little noses through the warming earth.

But to Cornelius and Trude, standing before their cottage door on one of these lovely afternoons, the charms of spring were wasted. Jenneke had just driven off after a brief, unexpected visit which left her parents a little bewildered and unsettled. She had come to ask them to make their home with her—to leave the little village in which they had passed all their married life! Quite unexpectedly, Steven's mother had gone to live with one of her married daughters, thus leaving Steven in complete control of the farm, and Jenneke had lost no time in coming for her mother and father. Trieneke, also, she wanted, for to her intensely loving heart it seemed that she could never be completely happy until she had all her dear ones with her. Steven had added his persuasions to his wife's, for whatever Jenneke wanted, he wanted. "I really need you," Jenneke had concluded. "Father can help Steven, and with the baby coming I'll be so relieved if you are there, Mother. Talk it over with Catherine when she returns and Steven will stop in tomorrow to find out what you have decided."

Cornelius and Trude watched until the wagon was out of sight around the bend and then walked slowly and silently into the house. From the fireplace shelf Cornelius took his long pipe, and settling himself in the fireside seat he gave himself up to thought. He might as well face it, he was getting old and Jenneke's assurances of his helpfulness were mere pretensions to save his pride, he knew. But he knew, too, that they were made out of a sincere love for him. It would be good to get on a real farm again! No one, not even his wife, had guessed what it had cost him to see his own little place dwindle to a solitary cow and a small vegetable patch. But it is hard for old people to make a change and he just couldn't decide. Besides, there was Mary Catherine to think of. Would she want to leave her home? She had left it once for them, and had come back to it at a sacrifice, he knew. Could they now calmly ask her to give it up? She and Jenneke loved each other dearly but would Catherine want to live with her? Well, they must find out how she felt about it. Whatever she decided, they would do that, and satisfied that he had disposed of the matter, Cornelius closed his eyes and effortlessly dropped off into one of the little naps he found so pleasant of late.

Meanwhile Trude, busily scouring already spotless pans, played with pleasant dreams. A baby to care for again! A half-forgotten lullaby rose unconsciously to her lips. Yes, she knew she could be very helpful to Jenneke who still preferred actual farm work to taking care of the house. Well, that is the way she had been brought up, and Trude frankly admitted to herself that she would enjoy a chance to cook and bake again. Mary Catherine did almost all the work herself, and her mother's fingers sometimes ached to get into churning and baking and scrubbing, though she fully realized that she was not strong enough to work the way she once had. Well, there was no use thinking about it until they talked it over with

Trieneke. It was her home as well as theirs. Whatever she decided they would do.

So it was that when Mary Catherine returned from Maeseyck, where she had gone for confession and to do some marketing, she found her parents happy and serene as always.

The spring evenings were still chilly, so the little family gathered around the fire after the supper things had been cleared away, and then the news was told to Mary Catherine.

"It is up to you to decide, Trieneke," Cornelius told her. "Your mother and I are firm on that. For us it doesn't make much difference, we haven't much more time to spend anywhere on this earth, but with you it is different. This is your home. If it had not been for you we would have lost it years ago as you well know. We have been very happy here in spite of poverty and hard times and if you would rather stay your mother and I will not leave you. On the other hand, if you wish to go to Jenneke's we will be glad to go. You stood by us and we will stay with you. You have been a good and loving daughter." Trude nodded in agreement with all that her husband said, and with one of her rare caresses, reached over and pressed Catherine's hand.

They waited as Mary Catherine sat silently looking at the dancing flames. So, another breaking of her life's pattern, as sudden and complete as the one a few months ago when Jennke had announced her intention of getting married. But this—this was wonderful! Now the secret longing of her heart could be fulfilled! She smiled cheerfully into the anxious eyes watching her as she said thoughtfully, "I think it would be wonderful for you to go to Jenneke's. I know that nothing could give her greater happiness than to share with you the abundance that God has given to her and Steven. It is right that you who have worked so hard all your lives should now have an untroubled and peaceful old age. And you will be happy there, I am sure. Yes, I think you should go. As for me,

I—I also have another home into which I think I shall be welcomed." She laughed and flushed a little at her parents' start of surprise. "Let me tell you all about it," she continued. "You both know nothing could have made me happier than to be a nun, but since that was not possible I have been content to serve God by fulfilling my duty here at home, and as you said, Father, we have been very happy. It is true that there are no convents but there is a way in which I can become something like a religious. You know that every month when I go to Maeseyck I visit with Cousin Catherine Palenburg. I told you that she is living with two other young women but I did not tell you why they were living together nor what manner of life they are following. I was afraid you might guess how much I would like to join them and feel you were keeping me back."

She stopped for a moment. "It's rather a long story," she continued hesitantly, "but I think I had better explain it fully," and at their assurance of interest she went on. "It starts about six hundred years ago when St. Francis of Assisi was living. You know he founded an Order for men and, with St. Clare, another Order for women. There were many people who loved his way of life but could not enter one of his Orders because they were already married or had such duties in the world that they could not neglect them. St. Francis felt sorry for all these men and women who desired perfection and so he founded a new Order for them. The people who belong to this Order and follow the rule that St. Francis wrote for them are members of the Third Order of St. Francis, and that is what cousin Catherine and her companions are."

"But," interrupted her mother in perplexity, "you said St. Francis founded that Order for people who had to live at home. Cousin Catherine isn't doing that."

"That is true," responded Trieneke, "and most of the members do live in their own homes, but you see, Catherine and the other women have no ties. They would enter a convent if there were one, but since there isn't, they chose to live together so that they could follow the Third Order rule more perfectly. Their Spiritual Director, who established the Order here a few months ago, gave them permission to do so. Of course, they are not bound to live there. They do not take religious vows and any one of them may leave any time she wishes to do so, but they are very happy together. They take care of the church, do up the altar linens, mend the vestments, visit the sick, help the poor, and in fact, do all they can for the glory of God and the good of the people. It is a lovely life and I pray that I may be allowed to share it with them." And Mary Catherine's usually placid face lighted up with enthusiasm and her clear eyes darkened with emotion. She went on to explain how each member was really independent, that each had her own furnishings and money enough to contribute her share towards living expenses. For the sake of order and religious spirit they had chosen Catherine Palenburg to be the head of the little household and had promised to obey her in such matters as concerned their life together. Trieneke assured her parents, too, that she would often visit them, and pointed out the fact that, for them, it would be very much as it was when she was in Father Borman's service.

It was late when all the advantages and disadvantages of the move had been discussed and weighed. They said the rosary together as was their nightly custom and then unanimously decided—Cornelius and Trude would go to Jenneke and Mary Catherine to Maeseyck. The little homestead would be sold and the money given to Trieneke. She was also to take whatever furniture she would need for her new home.

The next morning found them still of the same mind and then such a hustle and bustle ensued that it seemed no time at all until the day of departure arrived. Almost before Mary Catherine realized it the old folks were gone and she was left alone. She had no time to be lonesome as there were still several little jobs to be done before the house could be closed, and Steven was coming for her in a few hours. As soon as everything was in order she went for the last time to the little shrine of St. Anne where she had gone so often to pray. She stayed so long that on hurrying back she found Steven waiting for her with several of the neighbors who had come back to wish her Godspeed. From her place by the driver's seat Catherine looked at them. Their kind, pleasant faces had been familiar to her since childhood, but never had they seemed so friendly as now when she was about to leave them. Her glance wandered over the fields and meadows where she had romped and played as a child, and came to rest upon the poor little, dear little home. Sudden and unaccustomed tears blinded her as a surge of memories welled up in her heart. "Hurry, Steven," she begged, and with a final goodbye she was on her way. She hadn't dreamed that it would be so hard to leave. Ah, it had been harder for St. Francis. He had been put out and disowned by his own father but she had been sent on her way with the blessing of pious parents. Besides, it was good to have some suffering to offer, otherwise she would have been too happy.

Steven kept his mares at a good pace and before very long he was pulling them to a stop before the house to which Trieneke had directed him. Unlike the other houses on Capucine Street, its front door was reached by a small flight of steps leading up to it, which led to the inhabitants being called "*masoeurkens op de Trepkes*" by their neighbors. Soon she, too, would be a "little sister in the house with the steps"! She helped her brother-in-law unload and thanked him warmly for all his kindness, then she turned, and, with firm tread but pounding heart, mounted the steps that were taking her to a new life.

No gay young worldling could have thrown herself into a life of pleasure with more ardor than did Catherine into her chosen state of prayer and service. Wisely, she had determined to get the most out of this life by putting the most into it, and so well did she succeed that at the end of a year she was allowed to make her profession as a Franciscan Tertiary. Through the instructions of the Capuchin director, the Franciscan way of life which Father Christian had opened to her became even more clear and desirable and it was with the deepest love and gratitude that Catherine made her promises.

From the very beginning a change came over her and she reverted to the Trieneke of former days. The capability, the assurance and ease that she had developed during her years as the family bread-winner now gave way to the old timidity and self-effacement. There was no call for her managerial abilities or her skillful judgments. She took her turn in the kitchen when appointed; washed and scrubbed when the charge was given her; mended, repaired and made vestments and linens with the others. Her tenderness towards the sick and poor remained unchanged and she welcomed every opportunity to serve them, but often now, her time was not her own and she was not as free as she had been. In everything, she who had been the leader and provider was now at the beck and call of another, and she was well content to have it so. So successful was her policy of self-effacement that her years of capable household management were forgotten, and though loved and esteemed by her companions for her evident piety, she was allowed to remain in the background where she had placed herself.

Catherine's natural abilities lay unused but her spiritual forces were developing and strengthening under the wise guidance of Father Leonardus, the Capuchin rector. Like Father Christian he recognized in her spiritual potentialities that bore promise of marked sanctity. Believing that God had special designs on this soul he spared no effort to make it strong and courageous as well as humble. Catherine on her part confided to him absolutely and, though she carefully concealed from all others the lights and graces she received, to her confessor she was as candid in this regard as she was in accusing herself of her faults.

Catherine's happiness increased with the years, but since into every life sorrow must come she had to experience the keen pangs that come with the death of a loved one. First, her dearly loved father, and later, her mother, closed their eyes on this world. Though not a demonstrative family, with the exception of Jenneke, they had loved each other with a tenderness all the deeper and truer. Catherine was more than ever grateful to God for His loving Providence, which had made it possible for Jenneke to give Cornelius and Gertrude every possible care and comfort in their last years. As to their souls' salvation she had no worries. Their lives had been of simple, unquestioning faith and of rigid loyalty to the Church in the days when it was dangerous to be a nonconformist. Nevertheless, she felt their loss keenly and it was long before she could speak lovingly of "Sister Death" as did St. Francis.

So well beloved by the townspeople were the "little sisters in the house with the steps" that they were the proud boast of the city, and it was really not surprising that the report of their good works was spreading to other towns and villages. One June afternoon as the "little sisters" (now ten in number) were sitting in the common room working on church vestments and garments for the poor, they were surprised by a visit from Father van der Zandt, the rather new parish priest of the little village of Heythuysen, just north of them. All were slightly acquainted with him as he, too, was a member of the Third Order, and had studied his theology in Maeseyck, but he had never called upon them. Father was nothing if not direct and he came to the point at once. He wanted at least two Tertiaries to come to Heythuysen to work among his people!

"The children are running wild," he told them, "and are growing up to be utter pagans. You know that Father Todeman, the late Pastor, was in exile for refusing to sign the civil constitution. When he returned he was too ill to fulfill many of his duties and you can well understand that the religious education of the people received quite a setback, and consequently the parents are not sufficiently informed themselves to instruct their children. And the church!" The good father raised his hands in horror. "The vestments and linens are in a deplorable condition. My sister, who is my housekeeper, does what she can, but it is too much for her. In short, the whole situation is one that would appeal strongly to St. Francis —and you, his daughters, will you not come and help us?"

Sympathy shone on the faces of his listeners as he went on to tell them of other cares and worries about his little flock. He knew how to speak well and persuasively and he exerted himself to the utmost. He must have at least two of these good women, he told himself, as he looked around at the ten earnest countenances. Two of them—any two! No, he didn't really mean that! Not *any* two—not that one at the end of the table, not Catherine Daemen! A good holy soul no doubt, but definitely not the type he wanted! Now, that young, capable-looking person next to her would be just right. Well, he wouldn't have to worry about Catherine Daemen, she didn't appear to be interested in his appeal, sitting there with her eyes on her work! Man-like, the priest was piqued. As if she read his thoughts, Catherine at that moment raised her eyes and gazed into his for a second, but so suddenly were they lowered again to the work in her hands that he thought he must have imagined it. Brusquely he dismissed the thought of her from his mind and turned to more desirable and promising possibilities.

By the time Father van der Zandt had exhausted his subject several of the Tertiaries were ready to volunteer immediately, among them, he noted with satisfaction, the one he had already picked out as most suitable. Directress Catherine Palenburg wisely counseled that they should wait until they had prayed over the matter and received the advice of the Father Director before committing themselves to a course of action which they might later regret.

But the Reverend Father was a man of great determination and little patience and he would not leave without a definite promise that on June 21 two Tertiaries would make their appearance in Heythuysen.

"You must understand, Father," Catherine Palenburg told him, "that we are not a religious community and I have no power to send you missionaries. Those who respond must do so of their own will and henceforth they will be your responsibility."

Her words did not discourage him. Had not he seen the eagerness and sympathy displayed by most of the Tertiaries? There was no doubt at all that he would receive help, and as for their care, he and his people would see to that. And the delighted priest rode home to break the good news to the parishioners.

In the workroom tongues were flying faster than fingers as the women animatedly discussed their new venture. So interested were they that no one saw Mary Catherine slip quietly from the room. Anyone who had would have wondered at her unusual pallor and agitation. As one in a trance she reached her little room where she fell upon her knees before the crucifix. A long time she knelt there and when she rose her features resumed their usual calm expression though she was still pale and her eyes shone with an unwonted brilliance. Of what happened to Catherine we have no exact knowledge. She never spoke of the incident except to her director. But from their subsequent words and actions we do know that something transpired which convinced her that God awaited her in Heythuysen.

At the first opportunity Catherine gave Father Leonardus a complete account of what had happened. Her experience was not a surprise to the saintly Capuchin, who for a long time had expected something of the kind. "Yes," he told her. "Yes, it is undoubtedly God's will that you go to Heythuysen to the work He has shown you. It is not going to be easy. Father van der Zandt is a worthy, zealous priest, but blunt, impetuous and somewhat of a tyrant. Already you sense that you are not acceptable to him, that you are lacking in the qualities he desires. But what does it matter, child? God, Who calls you to the fight will also provide the weapons." They spoke together for a long time, this humble woman and the wise old priest, and the advice he gave Catherine then helped her over many a rough spot later on.

And so it happened, in the Providence of God, that Catherine Daemen, alone, was found ready for the sacrifice! How true it is that often the over-eager, the self-confident, fail at the crucial moment, leaving the quiet and unassuming to carry the burden!

The Bread of Life was broken for her for the last time in the grand old Capuchin Church. A final blessing from Father Leonardus, a quick breakfast, the parting from her dear associates, and Catherine was on her way. It is a strange fact that the human heart can experience simultaneously joy and sorrow. Catherine was deeply happy because she was fulfilling God's holy will yet, at the same time, her heart was heavy with longing for the dear "house with the steps" and all that it held. As the little covered wagon rolled over the cobbled streets, past the neat little Dutch homes, hugging each other in friendly affection, she thought of the people within—her friends with whom and for whom, she had worked for so many years. However, it was not in Catherine's nature to yield to idle regrets and memories and as they left the town and entered Napoleon's highway, with characteristic determination she turned her thoughts to the life ahead. Intuitively, she knew that Father van der Zandt would be disappointed when he saw her and the more so that she was alone. The day he had come to ask for Tertiaries she had sensed his attitude toward her. But—one must do God's will and trust in Him to make things right.

The long ride passed pleasantly enough and her driver being a man of few words, Catherine had ample leisure to plan, pray, and enjoy the unutterable calm and peace of the Dutch countryside. As they neared the village which was henceforth to be her home, she looked around with interest and thought how fitting was the name "Heythuysen"—houses on the heath. Sweet and spicy, the scent of the heather would spread for miles around in late summer. Now it was still coming to bloom but nevertheless it filled her with a sense of cheer. They drove into the little town and the wagon turned up a trim, shady street, passed the venerable old church, the wide field next to it, and the driver came to a halt before a neat, attractive home. Before the horse came to a full stop, Father van der Zandt and his sister were out to greet the arrivals.

Catherine observed the priest's face, alight and smiling, change to a darkening frown as he recognized her, and when she climbed down from the wagon the scowl deepened as he realized that she was alone. In the heat of his vexation the disappointed priest made no attempt to hide his feelings. "Why did you bring her?" he snapped to the driver. "You may as well have left her at home!"

Catherine's color rose high and the hands holding her bundles clenched so tightly that the knuckles stood out white against the warm brown of her skin. Never before had she encountered open disdain and contempt! Hot waves of humiliation rolled over her and her whole nature rose in protest. With an effort she forced herself to listen to *Juffrouw* van der Zandt who had taken her by the arm and was almost pulling her into the cool little house and up the staircase. Though she was hardly conscious of what was being said, Catherine was grateful for the chatter that gave her an opportunity to compose herself.

"And this is to be your room," the kind guide continued, opening one of the doors at the end of the hall. "You've had such a long, hot ride that I'm sure you'll be glad to rest a bit," and the tactful hostess withdrew.

Poor Catherine! So much zeal and love and sacrifice to be met with such callous coldness! A less noble soul would have yielded to bitterness, but the storm had passed leaving her only with a sense of shame at her own weakness. Gazing at the lovely crucifix over the bed she reflected that one only became humble through humiliations and that undoubtedly she would have plenty of practice if she stayed in Heythuysen. With a prayer for grace to do all and accept all for the love of God, she removed the dust of the journey, and with a smiling face went down to meet her Pastor.

Like the steady hum of bees wooing the fragrant blossoms, the soft murmur of children's voices floated through the open window of Catherine Daemen's little home-school. Resolutely Anna Marie Verkoulen passed by the house, determined that this time she would *not* stop. If only she didn't have to come this way. But—there it was. Every day she made a visit to the Blessed Sacrament and how could she help passing Masoeur Catherine's place when it was right across from the church? Often, as today, the window, which was flush with the street, was thrown wide open and it drew her like a magnet. She paused now, just for an instant and was lost! Glancing around quickly to make sure that no one was observing her, she did as she had so often done during the past year—retracing her steps to the window she peered in cautiously from the side. The sight of the girls and little boys grouped around their teacher was familiar to her now. Sometimes they were learning numbers, other times little fingers were laboriously tracing the alphabet on shiny slates. Today it was Catechism class, but no matter what lesson it was, the children were always so well behaved and attentive. It was really remarkable how this gentle peasant woman had subdued these wild youngsters. And how they loved her! Anna Marie had often seen them stop their most joyous games to run to meet Catherine, and perhaps, if they were permitted, to walk a little way with her, clinging to her hands. Their number was increasing and it was evident that Masoeur Catherine, as she was called by the villagers, would soon need help.

"Oh," thought Anna Marie to herself for the hundredth time, "if only I could be the one to help her, how gladly would I share her simple, blessed life." She knew it was a foolish dream. What could she do to help? True, she was a very good seamstress, but she had no experience with children, she was older than Catherine and of delicate health. "And in case that isn't enough," she reminded herself grimly, "remember you're lame!" It was these considerations that made her hurry past Catherine with a brief greeting every time they chanced to meet. She did not want to expose herself to what she considered would be a pitying rejection.

But today the longing to dedicate the rest of her life to the service of others as Catherine was doing was too strong. She couldn't go on like this—better to tell Catherine and have her put an end to the dream rather than to continue living in alternate hope and despair. Fanning her courage high with a quick prayer, she turned to the entrance, lifted the brass knocker and let it fall with a long clang. The sound of rustling skirts and scraping stools told her that the children were probably being sent out into the little back yard for a game or two and she knew that the door would open in another moment.

On the other side of the door, Catherine smiled to herself and whispered a little prayer of thanks to the good God. For months now she had been aware of Anna Marie's stolen visits and had sensed the struggle in the poor woman's heart. Each time she caught a glimpse of her at the window, she thought, "Perhaps today is the day Our Lord will send her." But always the little seamstress had passed by. She needed help badly and was very lonesome, but she feared to spoil God's work and so left it to Him, knowing surely that if He wanted her work to continue and grow, He would provide companions. So now with a heart beating only a little less violently than the one on the other side she opened the door wide!

In a few minutes Anna Marie's story was told. Her fears were put to flight and her longing more than satisfied when Catherine, after listening silently, took her trembling hands in her own firm clasp with a fervent, "Oh, yes, indeed you must come. God has sent you to me, Anna Marie!"

When consulted, Father van der Zandt approved of the arrangement. The good father had learned a lot since Catherine Daemen had come to him two years ago. He often recalled with shame the manner in which he had received her, and had kept her for several months in his house employed in all kinds of work except that for which she had come. However, even his disapproving and prejudiced eye had found nothing wrong with her competence or manner, and gradually he had begun to discern her worth. At last he had decided to try her with the children, and to that end had bought a little house where she could live and conduct her school. To his astonishment, she was from the first an unqualified success, and already the change in the morals and manner of the youngest of his flock was amazing. In the course of time (as men are wont to do) he congratulated himself on having discovered such a zealous, capable teacher!

Delightedly, Anna Marie was initiated into the mysteries of the school room, and with Catherine's unfailing help, she got along splendidly. Though the school was enough to keep them busy, they gladly acceded to Father van der Zandt's desire that they visit the sick poor of the village. Much of their precious free time was spent in this work of charity; many a morning one or the other started the day's teaching after a night spent by the bedside of some poor, frightened or neglected invalid.

They loved this work because they saw in each suffering

body Jesus, scourged, crowned and crucified. However, Anna Marie was not too strong, and so it was that the third member of the little household was welcomed not only with love but with relief.

One Sunday morning, as Catherine was leaving church, the woman ahead turned when they reached the font and offered her holy water. Catherine knew her slightly. She was Gertrude Kirkels, a widow, who some months before had lost her mother and an only child whom she had supported by working as a farm hand.

"Poor soul. She looks so sad and worried," thought Catherine as she accepted the holy water and thanked the woman with her warm, sweet smile. Side by side they passed through the big Gothic doorway, and immediately the widow turned to Catherine.

"Oh, Masoeur Catherine," she said earnestly, "how happy you are working for God alone, doing so much kindness for others. I am a poor, ignorant woman but I desire so much to love God as you do and follow in your way. I've worked long and hard for a living for myself and my family. Now I want to live and work for God and His poor and unfortunate. I am strong, Catherine, strong and willing. Father van der Zandt says I am only fit to take care of cattle. Perhaps he is right, but I do beg of you to give me a little corner in your home and let me help you."

Catherine's heart surged with gratitude. Oh, the good God! How very good He was proving Himself to be! Gently she took Gertrude's arm, led her across the street and into the little house. Taking the shawl from the bewildered woman's shoulders she said simply, "God has sent you here. Welcome home!"

Gertrude easily adapted herself to the new life. She had always been poor, so the poverty of the little household held no terrors for her, and used as she was to a man's labor, the tasks she was called upon to perform were simple. She scrubbed, cooked and washed happily, but her greatest joy was in sharing with Catherine the care of the sick poor. All the tenderness of her bereaved mother-heart was poured out upon the sufferers and nothing was too much for her to do for them.

Life was full and busy for the three devoted women. They worked hard and lived poorly, but not one of them would have returned to the comparative comfort of her former life.

Shortly after Gertrude's arrival, a young girl called at the house and asked to speak with Catherine Daemen. She gave her name as Mary Catherine Deckers and seemed both disappointed and relieved to learn that Catherine was not at home. She left, promising to return in a few days, but weeks lengthened into months and she did not come. The incident was forgotten by Anna Marie and Gertrude but Catherine often thought of, and prayed for, that other Mary Catherine.

At last, five months after her first appearance, the young woman returned only to find again that Catherine Daemen was out. This time, however, she accepted the invitation to sit in the little hall room and wait, and there Catherine found her when she returned from her errand of mercy some time later. Instinctively, she knew that this was the mysterious Mary Catherine, and she sensed that the girl was upset and unsure of herself. With her innate courtesy and tact, Catherine introduced herself, and taking the trembling, cold young hands in hers she said kindly, "And you must be Mary Catherine Deckers. What can I do for you, child?"

"Oh, Masoeur," the words came tumbling out as though they had been kept back too long. "Oh, do let me come here to live with you and your companions. I wish to live for God and others the way you are doing."

Catherine looked at the young girl thoughtfully, and liked what she saw—a frank, bright face (so like Jenneke's!) with innocent eyes that seemed more used to smiles than the tears

[58]

that shone in them now. But she must be careful; the girl was young and evidently in the grip of some strong emotion. Motioning her to be seated, Catherine took a place beside her.

"Why do you want to come to us?" she queried gently. "We are poor." She glanced from her own neat but faded attire to young Mary Catherine's embroidered apron and fine lawn cap. "Our life is hard. We live retired; we pray much. Our only friends are the children, the sick, and the unfortunate. We have no social diversions but live as quietly as nuns in a convent. I do not mean to discourage you but perhaps you do not understand our life. Tell me, Mary Catherine, why did you not return long ago? Why did you wait nearly half a year?"

The girl flushed painfully but met Catherine's gaze. "I was trying to get away from God," she replied simply, "but He wouldn't let me. I will tell you about it if I may."

It was indeed a strange story that Mary Catherine Deckers told that day. Though her home was in Hunsel she was in service on a large farm not too remote from Heythuysen. She was treated as one of the family by her employers and was very happy in her work and companions. Life was good to her and she enjoyed it to the full, with no higher aspirations than those of any of the young girls with whom she lived. One day she heard a sermon on the shortness of earthly joys. So eloquent and so convincing were the words of the priest that Mary Catherine was deeply impressed. She confided to one of her friends that if there had been any convents left in Holland she would immediately enter one! Needless to say, the news soon got around, and everyone was in high glee at the thought of gay Mary Catherine shutting herself up as nun. She was teased unmercifully, but though she wisely held her tongue from then on, she did not forget the longing that the sermon had aroused in her. One day someone happened to tell her about the work that Catherine Daemen and a few companions were doing. She felt within her an impulse to join these women, and with that purpose in mind she journeyed to Heythuysen to consult with Catherine Daemen. Her trip had ended in failure and the disappointment somewhat cooled her ardor for a more perfect life. Wholeheartedly she again took up her innocent but selfish diversions, and before long no one even remembered that Mary Catherine had once wanted to be a nun! And then, one night after a particular gay evening, she had a dream. She saw Jesus Christ gazing at her intently. There was no smile on His face; no tendernesss in His eyes. "Behold," He said with a sternness that pierced her soul, "behold the flames of hell. Depart from Me into those flames because you have not been faithful to your vocation!" Terrified, the girl cried out, "Have pity on me, O Lord, and forgive me! I will go!" She awoke trembling and bathed in a cold sweat, filled with such fear as she had never experienced in her life. Nothing could make her forget the expression on our Lord's face as He disowned her. It had haunted her until now.

"So you see, Masoeur," she concluded, "why I want to join you. It is Jesus Who told me to come and I must be faithful."

Catherine had listened in silence and when the girl finished speaking she rose. There was no need for further talk. There was only one thing for her to say and she said it. "Very well, child, come as soon as you can and we will try to serve God together."

With the arrival of Mary Catherine, the quiet joy of the household became somewhat less quiet! The older women rejoiced in her quick adaptability and zeal but were no less delighted with her vivacity and wit. To Catherine it was a little like having Jenneke again, so alike were their impulsive, generous natures.

Happiness, founded on God and held by mutual love and sacrifice, abounded in the little home, but there was no denying that the house was too little. Too, more and more children were seeking admission to the school and it was imperative that they have larger accommodations. It would be wonderful to have a larger place, but for that money was needed, and money was one of the many useful articles they seldom saw! Both Catherine and Anna Marie had a little nest-egg that had not been broken into for current expenses, but even combined the sum fell short of the price for such a house as would meet their needs. The project seemed almost hopeless, but trust in God makes a soul daring, and the firmer the trust, the greater the courage. So it happened that one evening as they were gathered around the candles, busily sewing and mending, Catherine said in her quiet, calm way, "We're going to move."

For a moment there was a stunned silence; then eager questions poured out—where? when? and how? Catherine's eyes sparkled with a glint of mischief at the effect she knew her next announcement would have. "I thought of building a house ourselves!"

"Let me tell you about it," she said when the exclamations of amazement and incredulity had subsided. "You know that dilapidated house in the center of the village?" At the look of consternation on their faces she had to laugh. "Don't worry, we're not going to live in that, but we could buy it, have it torn down and rebuild it again as we needed it. I've been examining it pretty thoroughly these past few days and I am sure that most of the materials are still usable, at least we could salvage enough to put up a house that, though not as big as the original, would be sufficient for our purpose. The main difficulty is that the burden of the heaviest work would fall on you, Gertrude, and you, Mary Catherine, and I hesitate to ask it of you."

Mary Catherine was out of her chair with a bound. "How like Jenneke she is," thought Catherine as the girl ran over to her impulsively, exclaiming, "Oh, Catherine, it's wonderful! I can't think of anything I'd rather do than build a house!" Catherine smiled at her affectionately and turned to Gertrude, who signified her willingness, not as exuberantly but as generously. After all, if they could sew, nurse, teach and farm, why shouldn't they do just as well at carpentry?

"Anna Marie and I will help you all we can," continued Catherine gravely. "It is going to be hard work and perhaps we shall often be tempted to discouragement but I am assured that this is God's will and that He will provide. I thank you for your cooperation. May God reward you for it."

Being thus certain of the support of her companions, Catherine broached the subject to Father van der Zandt. Greatly to her surprise he was most affable and graciously consented to the move. Though normally generous, he did not offer to aid them in any way, but, as one of them so aptly put it, his lack of objection was the greatest help he could give.

The transaction was quickly put through and with the remaining money a few men were hired to demolish the old residence.

What happy, busy evenings were spent in planning for the new home! When they arrived at an agreement as to the essentials, Catherine drew up a simple blueprint, and armed with this and the grace of God, these valiant women commenced their task.

Every possible minute that could be spared from school and nursing duties was spent separating the good material from the rubble and clearing the ground. It was not long until they were beginning the actual construction. If anything was needed to convince Catherine's companions that she was doing the work of the Divine Architect, it was enough to witness the real ability and skill with which this simple woman superintended the work. Not content with supervising, she lent a helping hand wherever she could whiie Gertrude and Mary Catherine courageously dug and hewed, sawed and hammered.

Poor, lame Anna Marie did her share by taking over all the household tasks. She was as eager as the others over the project but her faith wasn't quite as strong. "However can you sleep, Catherine," she would say to her often. "I'm sure I'd never close an eye if I had taken on such a responsibility." Catherine reproved her gently for her lack of confidence in Divine Providence and one day said to her solemnly, "Do not be afraid, Anna Marie. I assure you that from this little house many others will come before my death!" Mrs. Raetson, wife of the village mayor, was standing near, talking to Gertrude. Overhearing Catherine's prophecy, she laughed teasingly. "Now that really demands faith in Divine Providence!" Though she laughed, the good woman repeated Catherine's words to her husband that evening. "We'll have to watch this development," she concluded. "Who knows? Masoeur Catherine is a remarkable woman."

Day by day, during the hot summer months, the Tertiaries worked steadily, often watched by a group of curious villagers. Finally, when the walls had risen to their destined height, a group of men somewhat shamefacedly offered to do the roofing. They had at last realized that what was being done by these women was being done for the benefit of their children. Catherine accepted the offer gratefully, without even a temptation to reproach them for their backwardness in coming forward. With the men on the job, progress speeded up and by the feast of Our Lady's Assumption the construction was completed. Within the next few days Mary Catherine and Gertrude whitewashed all the walls while Catherine and Anna Marie followed with brooms and scrub buckets. At last all was ready for the furniture which they brought over with the help of some of the children. First the two large rooms for the pupils had to be furnished, so into them went not only the furnishings from the old school room, but the table and every chair and stool the Tertiaries owned. Laughter struggled with dismay when it was found that all that was left for their own two little rooms was a stove, a wash tub and some earthenware dishes. As they stood surveying their worldly goods in some perplexity, Mary Catherine pointed to the wash tub. "This," she said dramatically, "is three pieces of furniture. First, it is, well, a wash tub; second, it is our wash basin; and third—" here she turned the tub upside down, "it is our table!" Laughing, they climbed the narrow stairway, each laden with her straw pallet and thin blanket. It was dark up above, and the little cells were directly under the roof, but at least each one had her own private place, which seemed a great luxury and more than made up for the inconveniences.

When all was spick and span within, word was sent to Father van der Zandt who had promised to bless each room as soon as all was ready.

While waiting for the priest the Tertiaries held their own

simple ceremony of dedication. Sometime previously, looking forward to this great occasion, Catherine had purchased a lovely statue of Our Lady and a small spray of really beautiful artificial flowers. Above the front door they had made a little niche and now, as they stood on the walk, Mary Catherine nimbly climbed a ladder and placed the statue in the niche. Around the feet she arranged the garland so that each little blossom looked up toward the sweet face of Mary. One of those below handed Mary Catherine a heavy piece of glass which had been prepared beforehand. This she fitted over the niche to keep the ravages of weather from the statue. Surely not one of the earnest, prayerful group dreamed that a hundred years later others would stand in the same place, looking at the same image and garland, each as fresh and delicate in color as it was this twenty-second of August of 1828!

The young girl rejoined her companions, and in a voice filled with happiness and gratitude Catherine dedicated their home, the work of their hands, to the Virgin Queen of Heaven.

Father van der Zandt arrived, clad in surplice and stole, and together with a few of the villagers who had gathered to watch the proceedings, they followed him through the entrance which he blessed, and then from room to room. As Father sprinkled the walls with holy water and invoked the blessing of the church on all who should dwell therein, Catherine made a quiet prayer in her heart. She prayed that each thought conceived, each word spoken and each action performed within each room of this home would be to the glory of God, Whose loving Providence had so cared for them.

A sigh of relief escaped Catherine as she closed the door on the last little scholar. She did love the children dearly, but sometimes even the best were far short of angelic! Perhaps it was her fault, she told herself. Children are so keen to sense the least degree of change and she knew that she had not been her usual untroubled self for several days. She was a little worried about Mary Catherine. It seemed to her sympathetic and sensitive heart that all was not well with the girl. She had said nothing, left no duty undone, and yet there was something, something intangible and nameless, as though a glow had faded or a joy died. Never one to force confidence or to intrude herself, Catherine redoubled her prayers for their "Benjamin." Their life was hard, they lacked so many necessities, furniture, warmth, and sometimes even food. Catherine herself had no anxiety for their welfare—they were doing God's will and He would take care of them, of that she was convinced, but she realized that she was responsible in great measure for those who linked their lives with hers and she longed to lighten the heavy burden they carried. Anna Marie and Gertrude had each suffered much in their lives; it was Mary Catherine, the hitherto sheltered and petted young girl, who was finding the way a hard one. Today, Catherine was a little more concerned, thinking of the morrow when her three companions were to make their profession as Franciscan

Tertiaries. It was a day to which they had all looked forward with eager joy. Mary Catherine, especially, had nearly bubbled over with happiness until lately, when her cheerfulness seemed forced. Would she take the final step?

Catherine straightened the articles on the little table she used as a desk, and pulled the curtain over the make-shift cupboard which held the children's slates, counting racks, and sewing materials. Seeing that all was neat and orderly she passed through the little back room into the kitchen. Anna Marie was already there, trying to coax a trifle more heat out of the tired old stove. She smiled at Catherine. "Gertrude ought to be home any minute now," she observed, "and she'll be frozen. I do hope she remembered to tell her patients not to expect her tomorrow."

"She did, I'm sure," replied Catherine, confidently. "Where is Mary Catherine?" The girl answered for herself as she came gingerly down the steep, narrow stairs with her arms full of what seemed to be various articles of clothing. And so they were: aprons, caps, kerchiefs, and shawls of various colors, designs and materials. She was flushed and excited as she dropped her load on the upturned washtub, and Catherine's heart lifted as she saw the old familiar light in the girl's eyes. "These," Mary Catherine explained, "are odds and ends of clothing that have been given us from time to time, by the good women of the village. I have been saving them for something special, and surely tomorrow is it! Now just have patience until we see what fits who!"

Gertrude, who had returned just in time to witness the little scene, turned to Catherine in dismay, "Surely, Catherine, we are not going to wear this finery! What would people think?"

For an instant Catherine was nonplussed; she was somewhat dubious herself about the appropriateness of the garments but her innate good sense, coupled with the disappointed expression on Mary Catherine's face, led her to make the right decision and she answered pleasantly, "If we examine these 'fine garments' carefully, Gertrude, I think we'll find that they really are not so fine—just a little better than we are accustomed to—and what could the people think? They gave us these to wear! Besides, don't you all think that wearing someone else's cast-offs is true poverty?" At the nods of assent, she added gaily, "All maids dress for their beloved so it is fitting that you, too, dress becomingly for your dear father, St. Francis!"

Good, humble Gertrude was satisfied and soon they were busily and happily ripping here and tucking there; by evening three entire outfits had been made ready. To please the others, Catherine consented to wear a shawl they chose for her, but when Mary Catherine tried to get her to wear a pretty apron, she refused, and laughingly told them of the time she had worn a beautiful red apron to accompany Jenneke to the dance. Rarely did Catherine speak of herself, and it was with genuine interest that they listened when she did break through her reserve.

Catherine had given her companions thorough instruction in the Way of St. Francis, and in order to observe the rule as far as possible, she had several times taken them into Maeseyck, to Father Leonardus, her old friend and confessor. He had further enlightened them as to Franciscan spirituality and they had responded with ardor and simplicity. When they gathered together before retiring that night, Catherine spoke to them again of the grace that was to be theirs the next day. Her talk was brief and she concluded earnestly, "My dear friends, my more than friends, my sisters, tomorrow let us renew the offering of ourselves in a spirit of joy, and let us pray, pray not only for ourselves but for each other, that we may never desert this manner of life to which God had surely called us."

The day started with Holy Mass at which Father van der Zandt permitted them to receive Holy Communion. After the necessary work and a quick breakfast of steaming coffee, supplemented by a thick slice of bread in honor of the day, the four women were ready for their long drive.

They had obtained the loan of a horse and wagon from one of the men, and soon, with Mary Catherine in the driver's seat, they were bumping and jogging over the cobblestones. Here and there a workbound villager waved them a greeting, and their children, delighted at the holiday, ran along beside them for awhile. Soon they had left the town behind and were on the high road. November, usually so bleak and drear, can produce some wonderful days, and this November ninth was one of them. A thin, soft hoarfrost lay over the trees and fences, concealing the ugly bareness and transforming it into a winter wonderland. It was not cold, but there was a delicious nip in the air that painted roses on their cheeks to match the stars in their eyes. Gertrude and Anna Marie were on the straw-covered floor and Catherine in her favorite place beside the driver. Little was said by any of them but it was the silence of understanding and companionship.

Mile after mile they drove until at last they entered the city and pulled up before the "Op de Trepkes" where they had been invited to meet the other Tertiaries. Catherine had been at her old home several times since her departure, but never for more than a few minutes, and so she greatly enjoyed this visit with her old friends.

When the hour arrived, the three novices, accompanied by the other Tertiaries, entered the church. During the simple but impressive ceremonies, Catherine's thoughts traveled back along the path that had brought her to this day; her work at the pastor's house where she first met the Capuchin, Father Christian; her happy home in the "Op de Trepkes"; her reception and profession in the Third Order in this very church where she had received so many graces; the call to Heythuysen; the companions God had sent her and their whole-hearted acceptance of the teachings of the Poverello. It was a wonderful path; but had it come to a dead end? Was there to be no more than this? Had she mistaken her mission? Had she read into the message of three years ago something that was not there? But no, she must not doubt, nor grow impatient. God works slowly; her part was to plant, to water; God, in His own good time, would fructify her labors.

The formula of Profession being completed, Father Leonardus bestowed on the Tertiaries kneeling before him in the sanctuary the same blessing that St. Francis had given to his first followers:

May the Lord bless thee and keep thee.

May He show His face to thee and have mercy on thee.

May He turn to thee His countenance and give thee peace.

May the Lord bless thee. Amen.

As each now advanced to receive the crucifix, the badge of profession, Catherine watched her sisters intently. How earnest and peaceful they looked! Mary Catherine was pale as she bent to kiss the feet of the Crucified, but her expression was calm and tranquil. Catherine felt a surge of love and gratitude toward these simple, pious women, who by their generosity and sacrifice were lessening her sorrows and doubling her joys.

At the close of Benediction the new members were required to enter their profession in the records of the fraternity. This took some time, and on returning to the Tertiaries' home the little group from Heythuysen found a hot meal waiting for them. Needless to say, it was the best they had had in a long time, or would have for a long time to come! In simplicity they enjoyed it and all the other little attentions lavished upon them by their kind hostesses.

Time passed rapidly and soon they were on the homeward

journey, Dusk fell shortly after they left the city and before they reached home the early winter darkness was upon them; a darkness neither gloomy nor frightening, but soft and protective. It brought to their minds the beautiful psalm Father Leonardus had prayed that afternoon at the ceremony: "He that dwelleth in the help of the Most High shall abide under the shadow of God of Heaven."

CHAPTER . . . *ELEVEN*

It often happens that those who have professed service and
loyalty to a cause suddenly find their word being tested! So it
was with the little band of new Franciscans. November's beautiful, crisp days gave way to months of biting, blustering storm.
Winds tore across the heath, hurling themselves with fury
against the little house, their long, icy fingers pushing relent-
lessly through every crack and crevice of the home which had
hitherto seemed so snug and strong. It was the severest winter
that Heythuysen had suffered in many years. Children from
the outlying farms could not get to the school at all, and it
was very seldom that the village children put in an appearance.
When there were any children at all a small fire was built in
the schoolroom for their comfort. Other than that there was
no fire in the house except for the few minutes necessary to
prepare the frugal meals. This was not niggardliness on Catherine's part—there just wasn't enough money. The precious nest-
egg had gone into the building, and with the drop in attendance,
tuition had become practically non-existent. What little funds
there were went for a minimum of coffee, flour, candles, sewing materials. For breakfast the Tertiaries had only coffee;
lunch consisted of coffee and a piece of bread. Sometimes a
meatless stew served for their supper; at other times, bread
and potatoes were the entire menu. Catherine hesitated to ask
the Pastor for help. She knew that the extreme winter was

forcing many of the poorer families to turn to him for aid. There was no way by which she could get in touch with Jenneke who would gladly have loaded a sleigh from the well-stocked Suilen larders.

Sometimes a little money was earned by sewing or weaving for the more prosperous families. So desperate was the need that when an order came they all worked together far into the night to complete the work as soon as possible. Wrapped in their shawls the four women would sit on piles of straw on the kitchen floor and work industriously, stopping now and then to rise and stamp circulation back into their feet, or to rub and blow on fingers stiff and painful.

Daytime was bad enough, but the various activities generated a certain amount of warmth; the nights were torturous. Already stiff and numb they would climb to their little cells under the faulty roof. There were no bedsteads and the straw pallets were but poor protection from the cold and draughty floors beneath. Wearily, each one would crawl, fully clothed, under her single blanket and try to compose herself for what sleep or rest would be granted her.

And yet, with all these material hardships, Catherine would say, "How great is the goodness of God, for with all our poverty we are so contented." For herself, for Gertrude and Anna Marie, she spoke truly; Mary Catherine alone was miserable and unhappy. Young and strong though she was, the life was proving more difficult for her than for the older women. Always she had had sufficient and plenty of everything and now the deprivation of necessities seemed past all bearing. The doubts and longings that had beset her just before her Profession in the Third Order now assaulted her with increased violence, and she had not the strength to combat them.

Many a night when the peaceful hearts and sturdier characters of her companions enabled them to relax and get a small measure of rest, Mary Catherine would steal out of the house to walk in the snow, up and down, up and down, in an effort to coax her sluggish blood to a warmer pace. In the silence of the night and loneliness, her thoughts moved in a never-varying, self-pitying circle.

One night, returning to her room, she sat on the side of her pallet, utterly spent, physically and emotionally. Her mind, half clouded with weakness and worry, painted bright scenes of herself before a cozy fire, warm and comfortable; she saw herself at a well-filled table, surrounded with laughing friends. It was more than she could stand! After all, God could be served in normal comfort; one didn't have to be half-starved and frozen to love Him! At home she could be faithful to her Third Order promises; she could be chaste, diligent, kind to the poor and afflicted. Yes, she made up her mind, definitely she would leave this place in the morning—this house which was neither home nor convent!

This decision brought her neither relief nor peace. On the contrary, her heart grew heavier as she sat there, unmindful of the cold now, suffering as only the bewildered young can suffer.

Suddenly she became conscious of a soft rapping at the door, and before she could rise to her feet someone had entered and sat down on the straw beside her. Feeble flickers of light from her little lamp told her that it was Catherine. At the sight of that gentle, pitying face, the ice melted around her heart and the young girl broke down completely.

Wisely, Catherine waited until the sobbing ceased and the bitter temptation had been told. "You are right, Mary Catherine," she agreed when the story was finished. "It is a hard life and right now we are hungry and cold and tired, as you say. And it is true that the good God can be served in other ways—but, my dear child, He has chosen this path for you and me, because He loves us in a very special way." Simply, with deep earnestness, Catherine went on to talk of the mysteries of Divine Love and the value of suffering. Where did this poor, uneducated woman learn the secrets of the spiritual life? From her own experience of sacrifice and loving trust surely, but there was a greater strength and power in her words, and looking back on that night years later, both women realized that only the Holy Spirit could have enabled her to speak as she did.

As Catherine rose to go, she gave the girl a final word of comfort and reassurance. "You say that if you were a real religious, and if this were a real convent, that you could stand it, that nothing would be too much for you. Believe me, Mary, God has chosen our little group, you and me, Anna and Gertrude, to do a great work for Him. When or how, I don't know, but I assure you that we are to be together in His plan. Do not mention this to anyone, please, but if you are ever again tempted to leave us, remember what I have said." With a kind "Good night and God be with you," she was gone.

Worn out with emotional strain, but more calm and peaceful than she had been for months, Mary Catherine soon fell asleep. When she awoke in the morning, the world around her was just the same, cold and devoid of any promise of comfort, but she herself was different and her heart sang with the old joy and hope. Never again in all her long life did Mary Catherine lose her happiness in the service of God.

Living never became actually comfortable in the little house but it did improve. Before the next winter set in, faulty places in the building were repaired. The spring and summer months brought more regular tuition, and little by little the necessary furnishings were procured. What a great day it was when there were four chairs—one for each! And at last a table, a real table! Without a single pang of regret the old washtub was pushed into a corner; quilts were made for the straw beds. Mary Catherine made a little garden in the rear of the house where she raised such vegetables as could be dried for winter use.

Gradually as the years passed, their life took on a more settled pattern. Each morning they assisted at the Holy Sacrifice and received Holy Communion on all permitted days. The noon hour brought them together, and after the simple lunch they made a visit to the Blessed Sacrament. So cherished did they hold this noon visit that, even today, Catherine Daemen's daughters hold it as one of their dearest customs. Duties again took up the rest of the day until they met in the evening. All helped to clear up after supper and then over the mending and sewing they exchanged bits of interest from the various experiences of the day. No one enjoyed these family hours more than Catherine. Not talkative herself, she was an excellent listener, and each one knew that she was deeply interested in all that concerned them. From year to year, the attachment they felt for her and the ideals she stood for grew stronger. Her unwavering trust in Divine Providence and her ardent love for St. Francis became for them a sort of bulwark —with her they trusted and loved and were content to serve God in the only way He seemed to demand of them.

Each month they borrowed a wagon and drove to Maeseyck where they attended the monthly meeting of the Third Order Tertiaries. In this way their knowledge and understanding of the Franciscan way of life was nourished and strengthened. Catherine made use of this time to consult her old friend Father Leonardus. To this saintly priest she made known all the graces with which God flooded her soul, and she faithfully followed his counsels and directives.

During this time a great change took place in the political life of the Netherlands. Belgium refused any longer to be ruled by Protestant Holland, and rebelled. In 1830, Limburg, whose sympathies were with the Belgians, took an active part in the movement to obtain religious freedom. The rebellion was successful and nearly all of Limburg came under Belgian rule, with the result that the Catholic population became subject to the Bishop of Liége. Almost immediately the religious life of Belgium flourished; churches reopened, new ones were built and clergy were ordained; parish life waxed and grew strong. Monasteries and convents, closed since the days of the French Revolution, now gathered within their shelter not only the remnants of their once populous communities but also new and ardent members. Limburg, as a political unit of Belgium, shared in this blossoming of the Faith. As one little bit of good news after another reached the little hamlet on the heath, hope sprang anew in the hearts of Catherine and her companions. Sometimes at their evening gathering, one or the other would speculate as to their future. "Let us live as true children of St.

Francis," Catherine would say. "Then in His own good time God will provide." And His own good time came quite unexpectedly.

One afternoon Catherine slipped into the church for her daily visit to Mary's altar. Kneeling there, looking up at the lovely, tender face, she felt urged as never before to pray for the fulfillment of God's plan in her life. Suddenly there appeared to her the image of an old stone building, neglected, shabby, but with definite possibilities. An inner assurance told her that this was to be her first convent. As the image faded another took its place—the same old mansion but repaired and beautified, with large attractive additions and lovely gardens. She knew without a doubt that this was her convent as it would appear someday. The scene vanished, leaving her trembling and filled with a tremendous sense of joy and thanksgiving.

With all her dependence on God's providence, Catherine was not a quietist. Now that God had definitely shown her some part of His plan, she made haste to further it as she knew He intended her to do. The first thing would be to locate that building, every stone of which was firmly fixed in her memory. It must be around the neighborhood, she reasoned. Mr. Raetson, the mayor, had always shown himself most friendly and helpful to the Tertiaries and had often lent them his horse and wagon for their trips to Maeseyck. Catherine had no hesitation in asking him to drive her out into the surrounding country to look for a house that might do for them. For several hours they drove this way and that. His Honor found her a trifle difficult—she wouldn't even inspect several very attractive places which were for sale. She, of course, was looking for a certain one and nothing else could interest her.

At last, tired and a little discouraged, Mr. Raetson turned the horse's head homeward. They were approaching the village from a slightly different angle when suddenly Catherine stood up in her excitement—there, in full view, was the house she sought! "There it is," she exclaimed joyfully. "That is the place I saw and there I must go. There is where God wants us to be!"

The mayor shook his head—these women, even the holy ones! If she had seen the house before why did she wait until now to point it out? And what a place! Nothing compared with some they had seen. As for God wishing them there, ah well, Catherine was a good woman and if this was the place she had set her heart on, who was he to question it?

As they looked at the gloomy structure, set in the midst of unkempt grounds and surrounded by a dried up moat, the man appraised only a piece of neglected property, but the woman beheld a beautiful structure housing the King of Kings and a band of virgins who served Him under the banner of St. Francis.

The place was known as the "Kreppel," the mayor told her. No one knew just how it got that name, probably from the old French word that means "rabble" or "scum of the people," because, though originally a mansion, it had been used as a lodging place for soldiers and then as a prison. It was abandoned for many years until the present owner, a Baron Verduynen, let it out to tenant farmers. "You can see that they haven't done a thing for it. Absentee landlordism is a curse," he added frankly. "If you're really interested in the place, Catherine, I can probably get in touch with the Baron or his agent and find out what the prospects are. Would you like me to do that?"

Catherine thanked him gratefully. As it was getting late they did not get out to inspect the property, but Catherine resolved to do so at her leisure the next day.

The mare, no doubt anxious for her evening bag of oats, set up a smart pace and soon Catherine was at her own door. Dusk had already fallen, but Mr. Raetson could see Catherine's happy smile and shining eyes as she thanked him for his kindness. On his return home, the mayor as a dutiful husband gave his wife an account of the expedition. "You know," he concluded, "when she thanked me with that wonderful smile of hers you'd think I had just given her a lifetime lease on a palace."

Catherine had said nothing to the others about her experience in the Church. Now she did not mention the purpose of her trip with the mayor nor did they question her. But the next day when she took the children for a seemingly very long walk her sisters' curiosity was aroused. That was something she had never done before! That evening she told them about the Kreppel. "I didn't say anything yesterday," she explained, "because I wanted to get a better idea of it myself before I proposed its purchase to you. Not wishing to trouble Mr. Raetson again I thought a walk with the children would give me the opportunity to get near the place. Indeed, we made friends with the tenant and he permitted me to see a part of the manor. I'm sure you'll like it." Seeing her glowing enthusiasm, her companions were sure, too, that they would, and the prospect of having a home that might be a convent put them into such a state of joyful expectation that they didn't fully grasp the location or condition of the Kreppel. Nothing seemed to matter except the fact that their desires were on the way to being realized.

Never hasty, Catherine bided her time, waiting for a good opportunity to broach the subject to Father van der Zandt, but the matter was taken out of her hands. One day, during one of his occasional visits, someone unthinkingly let fall Catherine's plan for the Kreppel. For a moment the priest was speechless, then he burst into laughter. "You mean you want to buy the old manor house? What with, pray? Do you suppose His Excellency will sell it for an egg or an apple, which is about all you seem to have plenty of?" And chuckling over his own wit, the pastor left the downcast little group.

"I'm so sorry," the poor blunderer said. "I've probably spoiled it now." Catherine looked at her forgivingly. "Don't worry," she comforted. "That's where God wants us, so don't worry."

"Catherine!" Clearly and sharply the impatient tones of Father van der Zandt rose above the buzz and drone of Catherine's saw. Turning and looking down from her place on the ladder, Catherine saw her pastor glaring up at her. "Catherine," he demanded exasperatedly, "now what are you doing with a hammer and saw!"

"Building again," she answered promptly, coming down to stand beside him. "You remember, Father, that two young women have asked to join us. We need them badly and will be so happy to have them, but it's the old problem of no room. I'm trying to partition off spaces for their beds."

"Bosh!" the Reverend Pastor snorted. "All this botch and hodge-podge. Why don't you get a decent place to live? Right next door to us in Belgium convents are springing up like mushrooms, and religious life is flourishing again. Why should we in Holland lag behind? Buy the Kreppel—make it a real convent!"

Even Catherine's serenity was not proof against this startling about-face and she could not hide her delighted surprise. How many times she had urged that very move only to receive brusque refusals!

Recreation that evening was reminiscent of the one seven years ago when Catherine had calmly announced that they were going to build their own home. There was a deeper tone to the joy, though, on this occasion. The contemplated move was so much more significant, involving as it did not merely a change in dwelling but in their very lives. Often and again, Catherine had said to them, "Let us live as true children of St. Francis, and God will take care of the rest." Now her faith was being justified and it seemed as if their hopes and dreams were about to come true.

Lack of money was a big obstacle, but as Gertrude remarked, "It's an easier one to overcome than Father's opposition!" So they redoubled their prayers and it was not long until they had another sign of God's care for their cause.

Catherine was making a few purchases in the general store of the village when *Mijnheer* Cillikens, the owner and a good friend, surprised her by saying, "Catherine, not far out of town there is a large house for sale known as the Kreppel. The price is quite reasonable. Why don't you buy it and start a convent there? We would all be very happy to have real religious with us."

Astonished, Catherine could only look at him for a moment. The suggestion, coming at this time, and from an "outsider" at that, seemed to her just another indication of God's will. Mastering her emotion she replied fervently, "How gladly would I do so, *Mijnheer* Cillikens, but we just don't have any money outside of our living expenses, as you probably know."

"Well, now," the good man said smilingly, "I thought of that before I spoke to you. I'm willing to lend you a starter, without interest, and I'm sure that there'll be a few other men who will gladly do the same if you decide to make the move."

Catherine's words of thanks were few and commonplace but a world of gratitude shone from her expressive eyes, and *Mijnheer* Cillikens knew that he had found a fast friend.

Father van der Zandt was as delighted as Catherine at this unexpected windfall, and promised to contact Baron Verduynen, the owner of the Kreppel, to see what terms could be arranged.

He was as good as his word, and the next day he came to give Catherine an account of his negotiations. The Baron had proved most generous and considerate, quoting a relatively low buying price, and easy payments.

What happiness and excitement pervaded the little home when Father brought the good word! To their simplicity, all seemed accomplished, and even the pastor's announcement that they must first have the bishop's permission in no way dampened their spirits. Wouldn't the good bishop be only too happy to have a religious congregation in his native Holland and under his own protection? Father promised to write the letter of appeal for them and bring it over for their approval.

The province of Limburg was still under the jurisdiction of the Bishop of Liége, Belgium. His Excellency, Bishop van Bommel was an outstanding Prince of the Church. Though Holland-born, he so admired the Belgians in their brave struggle for freedom of government and worship that he became a Belgian citizen. As such, he was able to take an active part in the rebuilding of the religious life of the people, especially through education, and it was in great part due to his zeal that monasteries and convents reopened and flourished in northern Belgium. So it was with great confidence that Father van der Zandt addressed to his Lordship a letter in behalf of the Tertiaries.

It was a fine letter that he read to the little group a few days later. "Wonderful, Father," they chorused. "You have made it all so clear and business-like. Surely the Bishop will not delay in giving us the desired permission."

The pastor smiled a little smugly; he, too, thought it was quite a fine piece of work! "Humbly and respectfully . . . with which it has pleased Divine Providence . . . Catherine Daemen, a member of the Third Order of St. Francis . . . to seek a more spacious dwelling . . . could adopt a religious garb . . ." he re-read. Yes, quite good! Then a description of the property desired; the lack of funds rather underplayed but stress on the promises and possibilities! Finally, permission to have Holy Mass in the chapel.

Yes, he thought again, just about right—respectful, clear, concise. It should bring results.

Alas! Days passed into weeks until it became all too certain that Chancery was taking no recognition of the Tertiaries' petition.

Had Father van der Zandt known a little more about religious orders, or had he tried to see the problem from the Bishop's position, he would have realized that no church authority would immediately set a seal of approval on such an important project initiated by hitherto unheard of persons. A religious congregation has tremendous effects not only on the lives of its members, but also on the community of which it is a part and on the church as a whole. Therefore, it is of the utmost importance that the ecclesiastical authorities have at least a modicum of certainty that the proposed foundation is the plan of Divine Providence.

A calm, dispassionate nature would have reasoned out such a conclusion, but Pastor van der Zandt, though blunt himself, sometimes to the point of rudeness, was easily hurt and humiliated. Now he was cut to the quick by what he considered the Bishop's slight, and, as usual, Catherine suffered his displeasure.

Catherine said little about the affair beyond her usual exhortation to love and confidence but all knew that she felt the disappointment more deeply than any of them. However, for her, disappointment did not mean discouragement. Every spare moment found her in church before the altar of Mary where she had been shown the Kreppel as her convent, and it was here that she laid siege to the Heart of God by her submission and trust.

Meanwhile life went on as usual. Sometimes, when Catherine was not present, the others speculated on the future.

"I don't know that living in a convent would make so much difference," remarked Gertrude on one occasion. "We'd just do as we're doing now, taking care of the sick and poor, teaching the little ones, caring for church linens, and in general doing whatever we can for others for the love of God."

Anna Marie protested quickly, "Oh, it would be different, Gertrude. Just think, we would be truly spouses of Christ— real religious, not just merely pious Tertiaries. Our vows would transform all our lives and works. What a wonderful life it would be, but I'm afraid that it is just a dream for us. And we're not getting any younger," she concluded sadly.

Deliberately, Mary Catherine put down the bowl of potatoes she was peeling.

"Listen. It is not a dream. It is the truth—we will be religious, Catherine, and you, and I. I *know* it. I'm going to tell you something I have never mentioned to anyone because it is Catherine's secret more than mine, but by telling it to me I'm sure Catherine saved my vocation and perhaps my soul." And while the two women listened in amazement Mary Catherine took them back six years to their first winter in the new house, the winter of such intense suffering that even now they could vividly recall the icy numbness of bodies never warmed and the pangs of hunger never satisfied. At that time, Mary's companions had realized faintly that all was not well with her but neither she nor they had ever spoken of it. Briefly, now, she told them the whole story of those bitter days of pain and anguish to the last unbearable night when she had at last decided to return to her home. Simply, but with deep feeling, she spoke of Catherine's timely visit to the cold, bare little room and of her own overcharged heart pouring out all its disappointment and cowardice. "It isn't necessary to tell you all that was said by us that night, but I learned then that Catherine, though a poor country woman like the rest of us, is very close to God. I felt it strongly and the conviction has never left me. What I do want to tell you are her last words to me that night, the words that have given me strength and courage all through the years. "She said," continued the younger woman slowly and impressively, " 'Mary Catherine, God has chosen you and Gertrude, Anna Marie and myself for a great work. Do not ask me how or when, but this I know, and I assure you that someday we will be real religious!' "

Her listeners gasped with astonishment. Poor lame Anna Marie began to cry softly, and Gertrude's strong, work-hardened hands trembled as she tried to resume her work. For a moment no one spoke, then Anna· Marie raised her head. "Thank you, Mary," was all she said. It was enough.

One evening, a few weeks later, Father van der Zandt returned from his parish calls to find Catherine in the rectory parlor, chatting with his sister while waiting for him.

"Hello, Catherine," he greeted genially. "I've just come from *Juffrouw* van Meer's," he went on, removing his hat and coat. "Poor soul is quite ill and no wonder. I'm afraid she hasn't had enough to eat all winter. Why are people too proud to ask for help? Gertrude was there, so I told her to come here tomorrow and get a basket of food. I guess we can spare some, eh?" and he turned to his sister who nodded, smiling. "But as long as you're here, Catherine, you may as well take it back with you." He crossed the room and lifted down his big pipe from its place on the mantel.

"I'll be glad to, Father," Catherine agreed. She watched him as he lit his pipe, took a few tentative puffs, pulled his chair to the fire and sat down with a contented sigh. "Just like my father!" flashed through her mind, and strangely enough the homely thought gave her courage for the ordeal she knew was to come.

With another sigh of satisfaction the priest looked up. "What's on your mind, Catherine?"

Calmly, with no sign of her inner trepidation she replied, "Father, I'd like to present our case to the Bishop myself."

Black eyebrows drew together, teeth clamped on the pipe stem, and for a moment there was silence. Then, not looking at her, "Certainly, Catherine, you don't need my permission to write to the Bishop. If my letter did not suit you, go ahead and . . ."

"Pardon me, Father," Catherine interrupted, "but that isn't what I meant at all. Your letter was everything it should be. My plan is to call upon his Lordship and put our request to him personally."

For a fraction of time she thought he had not understood. Then the storm broke!

She listened quietly, only the paling and flushing of her cheeks showing that the whip of his words cut.

At his final "Get that thought out of your head! It is nonsense! Your very appearance would only defeat your purpose," his sister, who had been sitting silently next to Catherine, rose with a word of protest on her lips, but Catherine restrained her.

"Please," she said softly, "will you fix the basket of food I am to take?" Catherine's eyes begged compliance, and without a look at her reverend brother, *Fraulein* van der Zandt left the room.

Catherine faced the irate priest, feeling a twinge of pity, nor for herself but for him. She knew him so well. Not from any personal feelings against herself had all those harsh words sprung, but from his own hurt. The humiliation of his unanswered letter had dug deep. "I know, Father," she said, "that what you say is true. I am uneducated, ignorant, a poor peasant without grace of mind or body. But I feel, nevertheless, that it is what I should do, and I beg of you, for the love of God, not to forbid me."

As suddenly as his anger had flared, so quickly it died. "Give me your reasons," he demanded, and briefly, clearly, she did so. The priest was forced to concede that the Bishop did have a right to meet and to judge for himself the originator of the work he was being asked to approve.

It was never very easy for Father van der Zandt to give in, but after voicing a few objections, such as her age, the winter weather, the distance and similar obstacles that counted not at all with Catherine, he gave a somewhat reluctant consent.

But he was a man of surprises, and as Catherine knelt for his blessing, he said dryly, "Come around before you go—and I'll give you a letter of introduction."

Pale morning stars gazed down unblinkingly on Catherine, as with a final wave to the little group in the doorway, she started on the journey to Liége. Crossing the narrow street, she stood for a moment before the church and sent her silent greeting through the locked doors to the Guide in the Tabernacle. Far down the street glimmered the night light, its weak beam more eerie than the shadows it sought to dispel. Darkness pressed in about her, that thick, heavy blackness that precedes the first tentative gleams of dawn. With a start she realized that never before in her whole life had she walked the streets at such an hour! Houses so well known and so friendly in the day now seemed to loom over her like threatening monsters. No sound broke the stillness save the uncertain *klop* of her wooden shoes as she moved slowly over the snow-dusted cobblestones. It was with relief that she finally reached the open moor. Here she paused a moment to fasten more securely the shawl that Gertrude had insisted she wear over her short jacket, and to shift the bulky package containing her one and only pair of dress shoes, a fresh cap and apron, and a sandwich lovingly prepared and wrapped by Mary Catherine. Out on the heath the snow still was rather deep for February; here and there it had blown into drifts which caught at her unwary feet, making progress slow and difficult. It seemed hours before the day finally broke and she could see her way clearly enough to get on Napoleon's highway where the going was somewhat easier. Far away the sun appeared over the horizon, sending his long rosy fingers over the moor, changing each snowflake into an iridescent jewel. Catherine, so sensitive to beauty in any form, felt her hopes quicken and her eager feet moved faster. Reaching into her capacious pocket she brought out her rosary. Though its beads were large she found it quite a task to slip them through mitten covered fingers.

For several miles she made good progress when suddenly the wind came up, roaring across the open space. She battled it successfully for a few minutes, but she was tired now and the whirling snow was beating against her face, clinging to her eyelashes and obscuring her vision. A false step, a mighty gust—and she was lying helplessly in the ditch! For a few seconds she could not catch her breath, then slowly and painfully she crawled back on to the highway. There she lay for a few minutes before she struggled to her feet, still holding tightly to her bundle and her rosary. Putting the latter into her pocket she brushed herself off and rearranged her clothing. Poor Catherine! Her courage which had withstood and would yet withstand so many serious obstacles now almost failed. So it often happens that trifles loom large beyond all reason and threaten to accomplish what tremendous odds have failed to do. "Poor thing that I am," she said aloud. "I want to found a congregation, and I can't even keep on my feet!" Had she trusted only in herself or depended in the least upon her own efforts, she might have turned back, but always her confidence was in Him Whose will she knew she was doing, and on she pushed with a brave heart.

As if satisfied with the trick it had played, the wind fell as suddenly as it had risen; the snow settled back on its white bed and all was calm and peaceful.

Catherine hadn't gone much farther when she heard the

padded *tlop-tlop* of horses' hooves behind her. As she moved to the side of the road a sleigh drew up beside her and stopped. Young Father Scheyven from Nederwert hailed her. "Hello, Catherine! What are you doing so far from home and where are you going in this kind of weather?"

"I'm on my way to Liége, Father," she explained. "I have to see the Bishop on some important business."

"Well, that's where I'm going too. Come on, get up here with me. At the rate you're going it will take you two or three days!" Though Catherine would have liked to make a pilgrimage of her trip, she realized that the priest was right and gratefully she accepted his offer. He was a kindly man and when he discovered that Catherine had not yet broken her fast he made her eat her sandwich while he had a smoke. The miles flew swiftly under the mare's fast, steady pace, and sooner than she had dared hope she was within sight of Liége.

"Have you friends here, Catherine, with whom you can spend the night?" At her affirmation he continued, "I'll drive you there. I'm leaving at noon tomorrow, so if you have your business finished meet me in front of the Cathedral at that time. I think it would be better if you rode back with me. One can't trust the weather or the roads these days. Is that arrangement all right with you?"

Needless to say it was. In a few minutes Catherine was being warmly welcomed by her friends, with whom she enjoyed a hot meal and some hours of pleasant companionship.

After a comfortable night's rest, attired in her freshened clothes and precious shoes, she set out to attend Holy Mass at the Cathedral. She prayed longer than usual, preparing her heart for whatever was in store for her the next hour or two.

As Father van der Zandt had advised her to contact the Vicar-General first, she did so and found him most courteous and kind. He read her letter of introduction and then himself took her to the Bishop's house where he left her in the waiting room. Very shortly he returned and beckoned her to follow him. As she entered the Bishop's office she greeted him, fell on her knees and asked his blessing. The prelate bade her be seated but he himself remained standing.

"What can I do for you?" he asked kindly.

"Your Lordship," she began, "strange as it may seem to you, I have for a long time felt myself impelled to establish a religious congregation, and I come to you in the name of myself and my companions to ask your gracious permission that we may be allowed to assume the habit of St. Francis and follow the rule of the Third Order."

Bishop van Bommel was cool. "Ah, yes, I remember the letter from your esteemed pastor. Now, what funds do you have?"

Candidly Catherine admitted, "Myself and my few companions depend entirely on our work for our livelihood—we conduct a school for the children and also take care of the sick. When the opportunity arises we care for the church vestments and linens and do sewing for those who request it. We would like to open a small boarding school for girls if your Lordship will consent."

His Lordship frowned. "And just what education do you have? Are you or any of your companions qualified to teach? Do you realize that in our times there is a great forward move in education? Our Catholic schools must be able to stand with the best of the state. Could you meet that challenge?" At Catherine's reply in the negative he continued, "Then how can you even think of such a project?"

"Your Lordship, this is not going to be my work," Catherine was humble but firm. "I know I am entirely incapable either of planning or executing it. God has inspired me to undertake it, and it is He Who will provide."

The Bishop stopped his pacing and looked down at the woman before him, pityingly. These good, simple women—

what nuisances they were! That the woman before him was humble and sincere he readily believed, but he also believed that such qualities, excellent though they were, were insufficient for the undertaking she had in mind. Usually, when God demands a certain task of someone, He gives that person what is needful to perform it.

"I'm sorry," he said abruptly. "I know you are doing a good work in your parish, and I hope you will continue it, but I cannot give you the permission you ask. All the necessary qualifications are lacking; no education, no money, no security!"

Catherine's eyes met his bravely. He thought he detected a shadow of pain flit across her face but the next instant she was on her knees again asking his blessing. At the door she turned, "Thank you, your Lordship," she said quietly, and left the room where her dreams lay shattered.

The journey home was accomplished without any mishap and Father Scheyven took her straight on to Heythuysen. She was not expected back for a day or two, so her homecoming was a surprise. Catherine did not delay in telling her companions what it was their right to know, nor did she mince her words. Standing in the doorway she announced simply, "Dear children, I have come back without having any success. But we will go on trusting in the help of God. He is so good, so very, very good and He will provide." In spite of herself tears filled her eyes, as much for their disappointment as her own. She knew what a severe blow this was to them. In silence they heard the whole story; then one of them said quietly, "Well, we'll just have to work a little harder, pray a little better, and hope a little longer."

Father van der Zandt did not let her off so easily, however! He hadn't much to say when she reported her failure but a few days later he came literally storming into the house. "You've surely made it unpleasant for me, Catherine. Look at this!"

and he waved a letter at her. It was one he had just received from the Vicar-General, and it contained a rebuke, nicely, courteously disguised, but unmistakably a reproof. He, as pastor, should have known better than to encourage this impecunious, uneducated woman in her impractical design!

Catherine was truly sorry that she was again an occasion of humiliation to the priest, but she could not do as he bade her—put all thought of a religious life out of her head!

The letter ended with the sentence, "He [the Bishop] does not absolutely forbid the undertaking," and after the irate priest had gone, the question came up as to whether or not this left them free to go ahead with their plans. Some thought it did, but Catherine did not see it that way. "No," she disagreed, "that would not be the right spirit of obedience to the wishes of the Bishop. We will wait until we have his full approval. I feel that is the only right thing to do. As I have said so often before, let us live as true children of St. Francis and all will be well with us."

What was perfectly clear to her was not so to her companions but they accepted her decision, and not for the first time she uttered a prayer of gratitude for their loyalty and patience.

Some weeks passed during which a young woman, Gertrude Berber, asked to try the life of the Tertiaries. One day she offered to Catherine her entire savings of 3,000 francs. Hardly had they digested this bit of good news than another came their way. A distant relative of Father van der Zandt, desiring a measure of security in her old age, offered Catherine 3,000 francs if she would permit her to have a room in the Kreppel, provided that the purchase was made. Hard on the heels of that offer came another of 1,500 francs for the little house should they decide to move! More than half the purchase price was theirs now and Catherine asked Mayor Raetson to handle the negotiations for her with the Baron. (What a wonderful day it was when Catherine was handed the deed to the old manor house!)

Catherine's prayers grew more intense and fervent, if that were possible. Day after day, at her visit to Our Lady's altar she besought that dear Mother to intercede for her and to be to her truly a Mother of Good Counsel. No extraordinary grace was vouchsafed to her this time but she felt more and more that it was God's will that she again go to Liége. She had an understandably natural repugnance to expose herself to another humiliating experience, but it was a part of the price and she was willing to pay.

Father van der Zandt had no real authority to forbid her to appeal to the Bishop, but Catherine knew that under his rough and sometimes harsh manner he did have their good at heart and was eager to see them formed into a religious community, so she again asked his permission to make her request in person. The poor father was so astonished at her simplicity and humility that he was at a loss for words with which to deter or refuse her!

Once again the early morning stars gazed down on Catherine as she left the village and took the highway to Liége. Spring had blown her soft breath over the heath since her last trip: the roads were clear and dry; the white carpet had vanished, and in its place was one of soft, tender green sprinkled with thousands of tiny heath-buds. Dawn came early and suddenly; the air still bore the memory of snows until the full-risen sun banished that memory. It was an ideal day for a long, long walk such as Catherine had before her. She walked mile after mile happily. Not for years had she had so much time to pray, to think, to remember. As she used to do long ago on her way between Maeseyck and her home, she softly sang her favorite hymns and prayed her rosary aloud with joy. No one stopped her, no one noticed her. As she walked her thoughts went back to the days of her childhood, to Jenneke, and all the innocent, merry times they had. Her big, bluff father, and her firm, loving mother lived again in her memories. Her thoughts passed on through all the events of her life, even to the present moment. How good, how good God had been to her!

She made such good speed that, upon arriving at Maeseyck, Catherine decided she could afford a few minutes at the dear old "house of the steps" where she was sure of a hearty welcome. Over a cup of hot coffee and a slice of fresh bread, Catherine told her former companions of her plans and hopes. Encouraged by their sisterly interest and fortified by a short visit to the Blessed Sacrament, Catherine started on the second lap of her long journey. The time passed as pleasantly as before, and she stopped for a few moments' visit in the Church at Maastricht. She was tiring a little now and she still had a goodly number of miles to go. However, the day was still mild, and there were so many *intentions* to pray for, and so much to think about, that though she was tired when she reached Liége it was a healthy, happy tiredness. Once again she asked hospitality of the friends with whom she had stayed on her former visit.

Bishop van Bommel was in no happy frame of mind the next morning when he heard that Catherine Daemen from Heythuysen was waiting to see him. With no attempt to hide his irritation at her persistence, he went to the parlor prepared to deal with her very severely. As he entered Catherine arose, knelt for the blessing and then looked up at him with such a wealth of hope and confidence in her expressive eyes that his annoyance vanished. Kindly he told her to be seated, and then he too sat and listened to all that she had to say. This time he was more interested in her as a person, her life, her thoughts, her experiences. They discussed her project fully. As far as the Bishop could see, there was no major change in the state of affairs, and yet, somehow, these things didn't seem as important as they had before—not nearly as important as God's will which seemed to be all on Catherine's side! So with a kindness and pleasure that he himself later could not understand, the Prince of the Church gave her his blessing with the words, "May God bless your trust in Him; go and begin your Congregation!"

Laboriously, little Marietje sounded out the words of her catechism lesson but Catherine was not listening. Her ears had caught the sound of the opening of the side door; she recognized the quick youthful steps of Mary Catherine, the slow, deliberate ones of Gertrude, and last, Anna Marie's painful and pitiful drag. She heard them pass on down the hall to their own quarters. Forcing her attention back to the lesson, she endeavored to concentrate on the recitation, but it was a hard task. Her thoughts kept wandering to her companions who had just returned from their first inspection of the Kreppel! How she longed to join them so they could begin to make plans for their new home! At long last, the lessons came to an end; eager feet of children were scampering out to the street, while other feet, no less eager, were carrying Catherine to the kitchen.

One look at the sober little group gathered around the table was enough to wipe from her face the happy smile of anticipation. Her keen eyes took in Anna Marie's tear-stained face, and the grim, yes, grim expressions of the other two. She could not grasp it—never in all the years of their companionship had she seen, or imagined, these strangers before her.

"What is it? What has happened?" She faltered as she slipped into her usual place at the table. She turned her bewildered gaze from one to the other. "Please," she repeated, "what is the matter?" Mary Catherine turned away from the puzzled eyes bent upon her; Anna Marie broke into a torrent of sobs; only Gertrude, humble, sincere Gertrude spoke, but neither the tone nor the attitude were those of the Gertrude she knew so well.

"It's the Kreppel," she stated flatly. "We don't like it. We had no idea what it was really like—an ugly, dirty building, surrounded with smelly, stagnant water and unproductive land! We don't like it and we don't want to move there!"

Catherine paled, but she asked calmly, "Do the rest of you feel that way?" In response to their nods she replied, "But my dear sisters, what do we care if the building is ugly and dirty? We who have built our own home can surely clean and even beautify the Kreppel in time. As for the land, it can't be so poor; the tenant farmer makes a living from it. You must have other reasons for being up upset."

"Oh, we have, Catherine," sobbed Anna Marie. "You've no idea how hard it was for me to walk all that way and back again. How would I ever be able to make it in here to Mass every day or to make visits to the Blessed Sacrament? We'll be so far away from the church and I just can't bear that." And the poor woman who had borne hunger and cold without a murmur began to cry again, quietly, helplessly.

Catherine turned her eyes to the youngest of her flock. Mary Catherine flushed but she met Catherine's gaze steadily. "I don't approve either," she admitted. "It is such a big barn of a place and it's so far from the village. What will happen to the children, the school for which you have worked so hard? What will become of the poor and sick who depend so much on our care? How will we support ourselves if we have no pupils? And don't forget, Catherine, that we depend a lot on the gifts of food that our friends send us; do you think they will come all the way out to the Kreppel to bring us some loaves of bread or a basket of vegetables?"

"And that's not all," Gertrude broke in, "the tenant told us that he and his family are keeping several rooms for themselves for three years. We have more privacy here in our little crowded home."

"I don't like that part of it either," Catherine confessed, "but you know we have to submit to those terms because we cannot pay the full purchase price. It is just another sacrifice that we must make in order to attain our end. I understand all your objections, and I sympathize with you but I cannot believe that we will find them insurmountable. We have lived and worked together for a long time now, always with the one end in view, that some day, please God, we will become religious. That goal is in sight now, it is within our reach; would you turn back? Can we not make a few more sacrifices, trusting in Our Divine Lord Who has never yet failed us? I assure you that this step is a necessary one for us; it is God's will and I have no other choice than to fulfill it."

Slowly she rose and left the room, leaving an astonished group. Never had she spoken to them in such a manner. Always she had adapted herself to their weaknesses, her views to theirs, her desires to theirs. Now for the first time they felt the strength of her determination.

Relations were strained. Criticisms and complaints coming from the villagers increased the tension and added to Catherine's heartache. Humanly speaking she seemed to be standing alone. Her own household was against her; the villagers for whom she had spent herself, freely and lovingly, resented her plans to leave the confines of the village. Because of their own selfish wish to keep their benefactors in their midst they turned to sarcasm and ridicule. All the trials and humiliations of her life seemed as nothing to Catherine compared to this period of misunderstanding and distrust. Her prayers and penances doubled, her visits to the Blessed Sacrament increased and lengthened. "Help me, Lord," she begged, "help me to do

Your will—not mine nor theirs. Let there be nothing of me in this. Direct all according to Your designs. Enlighten us and give back to us our peace and contentment. I trust in Your Divine Providence."

Toward her companions she showed only love and tenderness but her air of cheerfulness did not deceive them. They knew she was suffering keenly, and because they truly reverenced her, they, too, suffered more, but they did not recede from their position. At long last Father van der Zandt became aware of the rift, and surprisingly enough he stood shoulder to shoulder with Catherine on the proposed move. Finally, on the strength of his repeated assurance that it would not be long before they would have their own chapel and daily Mass, the Tertiaries consented to leave the town.

Outwardly, at least, harmony was restored and all began with a good will to prepare for the move to their new home. In a way it was a greater undertaking than building their present one had been, it was so large, so neglected; and hearts were not in complete accord. However, the work went forward and every day found them sweeping, scrubbing and scouring the long, unused rooms and stairways. Buckets of whitewash were consumed making the stained and soiled walls bright and clean. It was a tremendous job, but after five weeks of constant work the day came when the actual move was to take place. Though there was little enough to transport there was too much for them to carry such a distance, and because of the unfriendly attitude of the townspeople Catherine felt that she could not depend upon them for help. There was one old man to whom she had shown kindness and who she was sure cared not a whit whether the Tertiaries stayed in Heythuysen or moved to Tibet. He had a wagon and a horse, neither in good condition. In fact, the horse was rather a joke in the village. "What do you expect, a miracle?" was the man's reply when Catherine asked if he would do their carting. "My poor old nag would drop before he got halfway there!" Catherine smiled at him warmly. "You do it for the love of God," she retorted, "and I promise you nothing will happen to your horse." He agreed, and soon the wagon was loaded; Anna Marie sat on one of the stools, clung to the back of the driver's bench, and off they went. The others went by foot, and when the old horse, winded, but otherwise sound, drew up in front of the moat bridge, they were waiting to unload. A very short time sufficed to carry in the furniture and place it. They looked at each other aghast—no matter where they put the pieces they were still lost! However, there was no time to worry about it just then as Father van der Zandt was coming to dedicate this, which was to be their first convent home.

Greatly to their surprise a large number of villagers came with the pastor, many out of curiosity but some with a belated sense of loyalty and gratitude. Vested in stole and cope the priest intoned the Veni Creator, and blessing the four corners of the Kreppel he solemnly dedicated it to the Sacred Hearts of Jesus and Mary. Thus, on May 10, 1835, the former prison became the future Motherhouse for thousands who were to be happy prisoners of love.

In spite of the beautiful ceremony of dedication, the Kreppel became no more attractive or desirable. Dampness from the moat penetrated the stone walls; the odor from the dank water was at times almost unbearable. The great majority of the townspeople were still displeased and determined to make their displeasure felt; very few children came out to the school; only one or two of their former friends remembered them with food supplies. According to the terms of the contract, the former tenant controlled the land but he allowed a small piece for their use and this furnished them with a minimum of vegetables. Harder than the physical deprivation was the loneliness. Though they had never lived a social life, never entertained or took part in purely social festivities, nevertheless they were on friendly terms with all and enjoyed the simple pleasures of neighborliness. Even this could have been borne —it was nothing compared to the restrictions imposed on their religious devotions. They managed to get in to Holy Mass several times during the week, but there was no question of making the cherished accustomed after-dinner visit to the Blessed Sacrament. How many times during the day each one had slipped over to the church for a hasty little visit to Jesus, or His Mother. Now that solace was denied them. Usually after the Mass one of them would stay in town to visit the sick and those in need of comfort, but these few hours seemed only to increase their feeling of isolation. It was hardest of all for Anna Marie as there was no question of her even going to Mass every day. Often she would stand at the windows from which she could just see the spires of the church, and morning, noon and night she would listen eagerly to the faint chimes of the Angelus as it rang across the heath.

Catherine had been waiting for a certain measure of material success before proposing the next step of her plan, but it was now borne in upon her that it might be this time of trial in which God wished them to advance. After special thought and prayer she asked Father van der Zandt to draw up a simple rule for them based on the Franciscan way of life. She desired also that at the time he submitted this rule for ecclesiastical approval he would also obtain for them permission to adopt a religious title for the community and to wear a habit which would be distinctively Franciscan. Both the pastor and Catherine were certain that the requisite permissions would be granted, but rather than take the chance of inflicting a further disappointment on the Tertiaries they decided not to tell them until the coveted approval actually came.

More than ever Catherine urged her companions to prayer and confidence. "Let us make good use of all these little sufferings and hardships that we endure everyday; the constant, unsatisfied hunger, the noisome stench, the dampness, the lack of privacy, the separation from the Sacramental Presence. Remember, God will never be outdone in generosity. Let us trust Him and live as true children of St. Francis and all will be well."

Summer passed with no word from the Chancery, and the autumn brought such heavy crosses that some people regarded them as signs of God's disapproval of their venture. Two young women had joined them shortly after the move to the Kreppel and the added companionship had been very welcome. Both were young women of promise and seemed to be completely happy in the hard life they had undertaken. Suddenly, the younger one, Angeline Kusters, fell violently ill and lived just long enough to pronounce her Tertiary promises. Her death was indeed a sad blow, but there was a measure of comfort and solace in the thought that one of their own had reached the goal for which all were striving, and they knew she would not forget them and their problems. The other case was far more tragic, and a double loss. The young woman became a mental case and had to be returned to her home. Not only was a promising subject lost, but also a good sum of money, as it was this girl who had made possible the purchase of the Kreppel by her dowry of 3,000 francs. This sum, of course, had to be returned to her as quickly as Catherine could amass such an amount, thus delaying payment on the property. Stricter retrenchments were necessary and, though the women were used to physical hardships and deprivations, all things together began to sap the newly restored harmony and contentment.

To encourage and strengthen them Catherine now did something which was very painful to her shy and reticent nature. She told them of her experience in the church when she saw the Kreppel before her, in its present condition and as it would look in the future. In amazed delight they listened as she described the beautiful edifice which would rise from the despised and humble Kreppel. "You understand now," she concluded, "why this move had to be made, and I hope that you forgive me for having to cause you so much pain and annoyance." Not one of them reproached her for having kept to herself that which would have lightened their burden—they understood.

Once more there was complete unity, and, as always, in that unity there was strength, strength for the present and for the future.

Ding, dong, ding! Gertrude paused in her act of peeling potatoes. "Odd," she mused. "That's the school bell but there are no children here today. Better see what it's about," and still holding the knife and potato, she started for the hall outside the schoolrooms.

Mary Catherine heard it up in her sewing room—once, and then again. Sensing urgency in the repetition she flew down the stairs, happy to have an excuse for a little sprint. As she reached the hall she saw a group at the front door; they were all there ahead of her. Catherine was smiling happily at Father van der Zandt who held a long white envelope at which the others were gazing inquiringly. "Hurry, Mary," the priest called. "We're waiting for you." As soon as she had joined them he opened the envelope and removed the letter, raising it so that all could see clearly the Bishop's crest! Satisfied at their exclamations of surprise and curiosity, the good Father cleared his throat somewhat like a bishop himself. "My dear friends," he began pompously (and who could blame him?), "sometime ago Masoeur Catherine asked me to draw up a rule of life for you based on the Third Order Rule of St. Francis. Fortunately I was able to obtain a rule and book of customs of a Franciscan sisterhood which existed in these parts before the French Revolution. I took a copy of the rule and after appending such precepts and directives as I thought would better fit your condition and occupations, I sent them to the Bishop, together with some requests which Catherine and I thought well to present to him at this time. We kept this from you in order to save you any further possible disappointments in case of our failure, but now His Lordship has answered most graciously as you may judge from this letter Catherine has asked me to read to you."

It was a wonderful letter! The rules and recommendations had been approved; Father van der Zandt was appointed their spiritual director, with authority to invest them in the habit of their choice and to receive their simple, temporary religious vows!

For once the pastor was tactful. Completing the letter, he handed it to Catherine with a few kind words and left them to themselves.

Tears streamed down Anna Marie's face, but this time they were tears of utter happiness. Gertrude beamed from one to the other, while whirlwind Mary Catherine threw her arms around each of them exclaiming, "I told you so! I told you so!" Humbly and reverently they looked toward Catherine, who by her valiant, quiet, determined compliance with God's direction and her complete trust in His Providence had brought them to the long-desired goal. Her own heart was overflowing with grateful love. How good was this good God of theirs! Never, never, would she doubt Him in the least, no matter how thorny the path He might ask her to follow. With a smile she beckoned them all into the little room they had fixed as an oratory, and it was only during their fervent prayers of thanksgiving that Gertrude realized she was still holding the knife and potato clasped to her breast!

Whole-hearted harmony and peace were fully restored on this memorable November eleventh, which date has become one of the most precious feasts in the history of Catherine's Congregation. Never again, though trials and hardships were not wanting, did they lose that essential characteristic of Franciscanism—joy. Cheerful countenances of happy smiles gave evidence of hearts attuned to God and to each other. With what eagerness they looked forward to the day on which they would be clothed in the religious habit, receive a new name, and begin to live a true community life according to the rules of St. Francis!

Much had to be accomplished before that happy day, though, and the first problem was that of the habit. Definitely it should be brown, but what kind of material, and more important still, what style? And the headdress! What a difficulty that proved to be! None of them had ever seen a nun. The only ideas they had were gleaned from the old illustrated lives of the saints, and even the humble Catherine quailed before the creations pictured there!

One morning Catherine called Mary from her sewing. "Come, take a walk on the heath with me, child; it will do you good." Joyfully, the young woman put her work away and lifted her little shawl from its hook. She loved to walk on the heath; she loved the crisp, bright November weather, but most of all she loved Catherine, who had been so patient, so understanding with all of them.

They said very little, but Mary Catherine was content to follow where her guide led until it dawned upon her that this was a very queer method of taking a walk. Every once in a while Catherine would stop, look all around, then move on, perhaps in an entirely different direction. At last the younger woman could restrain her curiosity no longer. "Whatever are we doing, Catherine? Where are we going? What are you looking at, or for?"

For a moment Catherine did not answer, then with a rather shy smile she replied, "I'm imitating our holy Father Francis. Remember how, when he was not sure which way God wanted him to take, he would walk around the countryside and take the first road that crossed his path? Well, I'm puzzled too. I don't know which way to turn to get material for our habits and veils. We have no money as you very well know. Perhaps our holy Father's custom will work for me!"

They stood there in silence, gazing over the frost-tinted heath. Suddenly Mary Catherine clutched her companion's arm. "Catherine! It did work! I'm sure! I just remembered that an old friend I used to work with has just lately married a cloth merchant in Weert. If they are in fair circumstances I know Anna will help us."

"Thank God. Let us take the road to Weert," said Catherine happily.

Mary's friend fully justified their hopes and a brown woollen material was soon decided upon for the habits, and a strong white linen for the veiling. "I'm so pleased you came to us," Anna assured them. "My husband will be as happy as I am to help you in your work for God. It will be wonderful to have real religious sisters and a real convent. Do not worry about the payment for this material. We are not pressed for money, thanks be to God. Perhaps someday, when you are well established, you will be able to spare the money, until then we will forget about it. No," the good woman expostulated when she saw them trying to lift the heavy bundles, "you just leave those right here. Jan is going to Heythuysen in a couple of days and he can drive out to your house—I mean to your convent," she added with a laugh.

Two joyful Franciscans left the little store, the warm glow in their hearts making them oblivious to the fact that the November wind had become sharper. Suddenly it was Mary Catherine's turn to stop and turn to Catherine. "Catherine," she almost wailed, "I'm afraid to cut the lovely goods. I don't know how to make the habit!"

"Yes, that is a problem," was the kind rejoinder, "but I'm sure we'll solve it, too. If you could see one I think it would be easier, wouldn't it?" She thought a moment. "Perhaps you have met the sister of the Pastor of Nederweert? A long time ago, before the Revolution, she was a member of a Franciscan community in Limburg. It was from her that Father van der Zandt obtained the rule and customs book he told us about. No doubt she still has her religious clothing and I'm sure she would let us examine it. We may as well go there right now."

The good old lady was delighted with the purpose of their visit and had no hesitation in showing her precious treasures. Mary Catherine felt tears of pity sting her eyelids at the tenderness and longing with which the old lady pressed each piece to her breast for a second as she took it out of the big closet. Every piece was carefully examined and lovingly explained until the visitors were sure that they quite understood each intricate detail.

"What did you think about it?" queried Mary Catherine on the way home. "Didn't it seem a little too complicated? We should have something more simple in our active life." Catherine agreed with her but that left them just where they were before. Not one of them, neither Gertrude, nor Anna Marie, nor their newest Tertiary, Frances Steenkens, had any definite idea as to what specific form the habit should take.

Fortunately, within a few days, they had a solution to the problem. Father van der Zandt had as his guest a Franciscan brother whom he naturally introduced to the Franciscan family at the Convent of the Most Holy Hearts of Jesus and Mary. It seems strange that though Catherine and the others had often seen the Franciscan habit of their Capuchin guides and friends it had not come to their minds as a possible answer to the habit question. But it had not, and it was only at the sight of this brother that the idea sprang up in Mary Catherine's mind, and she began mentally to adapt the simple garb to feminine form and needs. As she smiled and nodded during the visit, who could guess that her signs of approval were not for the conversation, of which she heard not a word, but for the attractive picture that was rapidly forming as a mental vision? More material—a slightly different cut—deeper pleats —fuller sleeves—a long scapular of the same material—yes, yes, it would work out quite well! She could hardly wait until the men took their leave. Off Mary Catherine flew to the little cubbyhole she called her sewing room, and for the next few days she was hardly seen except at meals and prayer. On the rare occasions when she did appear around the house it was only to whisk away any piece of goods, regardless of color or material that she could lay her hands on. Dust cloths disappeared as if by magic; an old common property shawl vanished; the kitchen apron took wings, and various other articles could not be located when wanted. Mary Catherine looked suddenly thinner. One might have been suspicious if one didn't know for a surety that no Dutch woman would ever go without her heavy, strong second petticoat! To all inquiries, discreet or blunt, she was very deaf indeed!

One afternoon, when all except Mary Catherine were busy in the workroom mending the church linens, a little self-conscious cough caused them to look up. What a sensation! No great actress ever had a more dramatic entrance than had plain Mary Catherine Deckers as she slowly advanced into the room and even more slowly pivoted before the astonished gaze of her spell-bound audience. Again she turned, and again, showing to full advantage the long, simple garment, confined into folds at the waist, the wide open sleeves, the long scapular falling front and back to the full length of the dress. True, the ensemble was like Jacob's coat of many colors! There were the missing dusters, the shawl, the apron! Gertrude's treasured piece of stout rope, so handy for many things, was doing duty as a cord—and even to the most innocent, the striped material in the scapular looked suspiciously like that of a second skirt! But what of that! Each feminine eye beheld the creation not as it was, but as it should be; the beautiful brown, falling simply to the feet; the white woolen cord with its symbolic knots; the graceful scapular that gave the needed feminine touch to the masculine habit.

There probably never was a woman, young or old, religious or secular, who could remain unaffected at the sight of a new garment. It just does something to her spirits that a man can never understand. But if that garment is one that has been dreamed of and longed for over a period of years, it assumes an importance seemingly out of all proportion to all but those intimately concerned. So, with laughter and tears, another milestone on the path to religious life was reached and passed.

Father van der Zandt dropped in that afternoon, quite unprepared, poor man, for the surprise that was to be his. Even his stolidity was shattered when he was confronted with a multi-colored apparition! It took an amount of explanation and assurance before he could be even slightly convinced that the "witch's costume" as he so bluntly called it, would really turn out to be a neat, attractive habit. Still skeptical, he gave a somewhat reluctant approval, upon which Mary Catherine immediately set to work before he could change his mind!

All fingers flew swiftly now. Mary cut out the five habits and scapulars and each one helped whenever and wherever she could. They decided to adopt several of the details of the habit worn by the former religious, whom they had earlier consulted. Thus, on the breast of each scapular was sewn a black cross with the implements of the Passion. Though the form of the veiling was the same, a square guimpe, a forehead bandeau, and a piece of the white material framing the face, Mary Catherine decided that a little starch would not only make the veiling neater but that it would stay cleaner. A simple black veil was to be draped over the head.

Catherine visited the old ex-nun several times, and always she had something of interest to relate during the busy sewing period. One time it was the history of the Order to which the former sister belonged, and to which they themselves now owed so much. The congregation had been founded in the early seventeenth century by a very saintly woman, Mother Johanna, who had come from Ghent to Limburg to establish her sisterhood, which she called "The Penitents." The Penitents were, of course, cloistered religious, and they followed the rule for the Third Order as adapted to religious communities. Their constitutions were framed by their spiritual father, Reverend Peter Marchant, O.F.M., one of the glories of the Franciscan Order.

"So you see," Catherine concluded, "though we are perhaps the youngest of the large Franciscan family, nevertheless we will be able to trace many of our precepts and customs back more than two hundred years."

"Love your habit dearly," she said to them on another occasion. "It is just a simplified form of the Penitents and we might say it is Our Lady's choice. There was a tradition in that Congregation that at one time when Mother Johanna was sorely perplexed as to what type of habit her sisters should wear, the Blessed Mother appeared to her clothed in a brown habit and scapular such as we are preparing now. Our heavenly Mother wore a headdress such as ours, her feet were bare and she had on wooden sandals."

"Oh, let us wear sandals, too," someone suggested.

"I did speak to Father about that," Catherine admitted. "He gave us permission to wear sandals, if all agree. Remember, it will be very hard in the winter, so think it over and let me know how you feel about it."

Anyone entering the common room those last days of January was likely to be met with a veritable litany of the saints! "Mary," "Frances," "Victoria," "Clare," "Elizabeth," "Leo" and other such names were flying back and forth. All were lovely, each represented the chosen friends of God, and yet it was so hard to choose. Each one felt that the choice was such an individual and important affair that there must be one that was just right for her, and so the search and discussions went on for days. As each reached a decision, without saying a word to any of the others, she would go to Catherine, feeling, and rightly so, that their Mother should have first choice. But to each she said lovingly, "No, child, that is not the name for me. You take it, and may your holy patron be a true friend and model to you."

At last came the day when the last habit was hung up and the last veiling put carefully away for the great day.

"Now, may we tell each other our new names?" asked Frances Steenkens.

"All right, Frances," answered Catherine, "suppose you begin."

"I have chosen Angeline," said the young girl.

"And mine is Frances," beamed Mary Catherine.

"I will be called Anthony," came from the solemn Gertrude.

Anna Marie was next. "I am taking Clare."

Each name was met with suitable comments of approval, and now all eyes turned to Catherine. What had she chosen? She had not wanted Francis, nor Anthony, nor Clare, those names so inextricably bound up in the origin of the Order. Would it be Leo—good, dear Brother Leo, or Giles, the simple, humble friend of Francis? Perhaps it might be Juniper of whom Francis had said, "I wish I had a forest of such Junipers."

Without raising her eyes from her knitting, Catherine said quietly, "You have all chosen well, sisters. I, too, will have a wonderful patron. My name in religion will be Magdalen."

Magdalen? Her listeners were disconcerted and disappointed. Magdalen! Why it wasn't even remotely Franciscan!

But Catherine smiled to herself. Penitent, loving, faithful Magdalen would be just the patron for poor, ignorant, trusting Catherine Daemen.

"See, here they come!" "They're coming!" "They're coming!" The excited whispers flew from one group to another until even those standing at the foot of the church steps stopped their chatter and stretched toward the wide open church doors. Anyone seeing the great number of people around the church would have thought it one of the major feasts as surely all Catholic Heythuysen was there! But it was just an ordinary day—Tuesday, February 11, 1836, to be exact. The only thing extraordinary about it was the little group of religious sisters that had just come from inside the church and was standing on the top step before the great doors.

For a moment there was a hush as the crowd took in the picture before them: five women in long brown gowns, white headdresses and black veils. These were the very first nuns that any except the very oldest among them had ever seen, and with exclamations of joy they approached the familiar strangers. Reverently they fingered the woollen habit, the white cord, and stared at the bare feet in the wooden sandals. From one sister to another they passed, repeating the new name of each with childlike relish: Sister Magdalen, their dear Masoeur Catherine; Sister Anthony, the one-time widow Kirkels; Sister Clara, little, lame Anna Marie; Sister Frances, the gay and vivacious Mary Catherine; and lastly, Sister Angeline, the young Mary Frances Steenkens, who not long before had been one of themselves.

The recipients of all this attention were delighted that at last the barrier between themselves and the townspeople had broken down. Now they felt truly at ease with these old friends of theirs, and each one did her best to answer all the questions that friendly curiosity proposed. It was Father van der Zandt who finally rescued the sisters by reminding the people that it was getting late and the sisters had not yet broken their fast. Needless to say, there was no walking for them that day. Each one could have had her choice of half a dozen vehicles in which to ride out to the Kreppel!

What a surprise it was when on reaching the convent they found a number of women there before them, each carrying "a little something for the sisters' dinner"! More followed and the "little something" grew into such proportions that Sister Anthony was able to prepare nourishing meals for the rest of the week!

It was early afternoon before the last well-wisher left and they had time to take stock of themselves. What a thrill it was to really see each other in the already dear Franciscan habit and to call each other by the lovely title "Sister." They had been practicing that for days, and for several hours there wasn't one slip! Some good ladies had already set the table and loaded it with succulent dishes, the likes of which they had never seen since their lot had been cast together, and they proceeded to enjoy immensely what the good God had sent them.

Sister Magdalen gave a start as she looked down at a dish of *balkenbrei* at her place. *Balkenbrei!* She had not even seen it for ages! Her thoughts flew back across the years to the days when, on special occasions, *balkenbrei* was made in the Daemen cottage. She could see herself, the little Trieneke, helping her mother eagerly while listening to the calm voice recount the ever-fascinating story of Mary Catherine's birth and baptism. She remembered well that, according to the story, Aunt Mary had made *balkenbrei* for her mother and father the day she was born. And now, so many miles and years away from those days, she could almost hear her mother's concluding words, "You must have a great trust in the good God, my daughter!" With all her heart she now re-echoed the words with which she had answered her mother, "I will always trust Him," and as she looked around the table at the faces of her daughters smiling happily in their white frames she felt again that sudden upsurge of confidence in Divine Providence that seemed almost too strong for her heart to hold.

With an effort she pulled herself to attention. Sister Anthony was commenting on the kindness of the pastor who had sung the Mass of the Holy Ghost for them that morning after he had given them the holy habit. Sister Frances confessed that she was so nervous she thought she would never get the veil on! All were very happy at the spirit of friendliness displayed by the good villagers.

"I'm sure that many of the children will come back to us now," remarked Sister Clara. "The people just did not understand what we wanted to do and it hurt and offended them when we moved away from the village. Now they realize what our purpose was and I think they are really proud of us!"

At last the precious day came to a close, and after night prayers they knelt a long time, reliving not only the day but the events of the past few years. One by one they left until Catherine was alone. She had so much to say to Him, and so much more to hear from Him, that it was quite late when she made her way down the dark hall to her cell. There was still one more task she had to perform before going to rest. Lighting her candle stub she took down the copy book she used for her records; the events of this day must be entered. She wrote with her usual care and precision and as she inscribed the last entry,

"I, Mary Catherine Daemen (the last time she would so sign herself!) renounce my inheritance and give it to the convent," she had to smile. This was one case where the deed had long preceded the promise!

When Father van der Zandt dropped in on his spiritual daughters a few days later he found a slightly bewildered group going through the process of adjustment. Dressing in a habit and veil was proving quite a different process from that to which they had been used to all their lives! Nothing seemed to fit the way it should! Caps had just been put on and they always looked right, but a guimpe and a veil! When each saw the others those first few days she realized only too well what a sight she presented! There was not a trace of vanity in any of these women and yet they didn't know whether to be glad or sorry that they didn't have mirrors! Because they were not yet used to the heavy, confining robes, the full sleeves and the scapular, their work was impeded. And worst of all, so they thought, the old names would crop out.

This recital of their woes gave the pastor a hearty laugh but he was not really unsympathetic to them and assured them that all was perfectly natural and there was nothing that time would not cure.

He now officially appointed Sister Magdalen as their superior and she accepted the office with her usual equanimity and humility. She knew that this, too, was still a part of God's plan.

One of her first acts was to welcome to the Convent of the Most Holy Hearts of Jesus and Mary the old ex-sister from Nederwert. Some time before she had invited the old lady to stay with the sisters for a while to train them in convent customs and usages of which they were totally ignorant. As a result of her daily instructions their life began to take on a completely different form. Not one of them had realized the great difference between a merely communal life and life under a religious rule. Even the oldest had been a mere child at the time of the Revolution which had dispersed religious orders, and not one of them had ever seen a convent or a nun, and so they had much to learn. The lessons seemed almost endless: their old friend and sister must now be called "Mother"; they must learn to sit, walk, eat, talk, with religious decorum; to perform many acts of humility and penance; to follow their own wills in nothing. Freedom of action was a thing of the past. No more could Gertrude, Sister Anthony, strike off across the heath to visit the sick of the village without permission from the superior. Mary Catherine had to learn to control her flying feet and equally eager tongue. Gone was the somewhat free family existence, and in its place was developing an orderly well-regulated religious life. It was hard but they loved it— every minute and every iota of it. It was what they had all been striving for, the hope that had buoyed them during the long hard years, the life to which they knew they had been called, and they threw themselves into it with great love and determination. In spite of the restrictions, or more correctly, because of them, hearts were lighter, recreations gayer and charity sweeter.

During these days the title of the little congregation was decided upon; Franciscan Sisters of Penance. Also, as they learned more about the rule of the Penitents as expounded by their instructress, they incorporated more of it into their own constitutions and manner of life. Father van der Zandt proved his true worth and religious spirit in the drafting of the Constitution.

A great source of joy to the sisters these days was the evidence of the restored friendship of the people of Heythuysen. Once again the needed gifts of vegetables, milk and flour found their way to the convent and, best of all, many of the old pupils returned along with several new ones. The added income was a necessity now more than ever, as several young girls from the neighboring towns had asked to be admitted into the new congregation and provision must be made for them. Several of these girls were able to bring a modest dowry and soon Mother Magdalen found herself in a position to pay off some of the debts. She did this gladly, and trusting in her never failing Providence, she began a small scale program of building and renovation. Some of the larger rooms were partitioned off into individual cells and in this way provision was made for at least eleven more members. The northwest wing had one room that was exceptionally large and this she intended to convert into a chapel that would serve until a new wing could be built. When word of this project spread across the heath to the bordering towns, the good people, grateful to have a home of religious women among them, presented the sisters with many of the necessary appointments. From Hessel came a beautiful set of vestments; from another town, a small but adequate altar; and from still another, candlesticks, vases and so on. The sisters themselves made the necessary linens. One day a beautiful little church bell was received from an unknown benefactor with a request for prayers. Since there was no place to put it, Mother Magdalen purchased some sun-baked bricks and had a little bell-tower built over the temporary chapel.

No one was happier over this gift than Sister Clara. Listening to its thrice-daily Angelus call she remembered how, just a few short months before, she used to wait avidly and tearfully, to catch the faint tones of the village church bells as they came across the heath, and remembering, she was ashamed. Truly, as Mother Magdalen so often said, "God is good. So very, very good."

Pride and admiration for the little community's progress emboldened Father van der Zandt to write fully to the Bishop of their advances and prospects. He earnestly petitioned his Lordship to sanction their private chapel, and carried away by his zeal he even dared to suggest that the Bishop might appoint some priest to be chaplain at the Convent!

This was a venturesome request for a community not yet a year old, and no one was more surprised than the pastor himself when a letter from the Vicar-General informed him that not only did the Bishop grant permission for the chapel but also had appointed Father John van Kessel to be chaplain at the Convent of the Most Holy Hearts of Jesus and Mary!

According to this letter, which was received on the third of May, the chaplain would arrive on the sixth. This didn't leave much time to prepare for the big event but all set to work with a hearty will. Everyone agreed that Father van der Zandt should be the one formally to bless the new chapel and offer the first Holy Mass, and the good priest was delighted to do so. Since this couldn't be any later than May fifth it gave the sisters two days in which to prepare the room Mother Magdalen had chosen. It had already been cleaned and white-washed. The little altar was soon put in place and all insisted that Mother Magdalen should be the one to prepare the sacred vessels and vestments, but each had some share in beautifying the spot that was so soon to become the heart of their home. The two young girls, or postulants as they were called, gaily made off for the village where they begged flowers from the good people. The response was overwhelming. They returned literally bent under the weight of their sweet burdens! Flushed and excited over their success, they called Mother Magdalen to view their treasures, and her smile of appreciation and delight seemed to them more beautiful than their loveliest blossoms.

May sent one of her most beautiful days, soft, fragrant, delicate. Within the little chapel, all was equally fitting. In prayerful expectancy the small group of worshippers waited, kneeling on the shining floor, sisters on one side, faithful villagers on the other. Suddenly chimes pealed from the little bell-tower, joyfully calling: "He's coming!" He's coming!" Hardly had their echoes died away when Father van der Zandt appeared, clothed in surplice and cope. The blessing, short but impressive, was followed immediately by the sacrifice of the Mass—the first of hundreds that were to be offered in that simple room.

After the services, the good women visitors took the opportunity of examining every detail of the sisters' home. Two things struck them forcibly: the absolute cleanliness (which pleased their Dutch hearts) and the utter poverty. Horrified exclamations passed from mouth to mouth over the totally bare floors, some of which were of brick; over the straw beds, the backless chairs, and the one large homemade table. It is true, there wasn't one superfluous article, but the sisters hadn't felt especially poor.

Sister Frances grinned at Sister Anthony. "They should have seen our triple-service washtub of the old days," she whispered under cover of the women's chatter.

Unexpected and embarrassing as it was, this little visitation had several good results, not the least of which was the increased admiration and thoughtfulness of their old friends.

Father van Kessel arrived the next day, and from the moment he met the community until his transfer, four years later, he proved a kind and devoted friend to them.

A few days later, on May 10, the sisters celebrated their first birthday in the Kreppel. It was a day of boundless gratitude for the graces that had been bestowed upon them in that one eventful year. On May 10, 1835, they had been a group of pious women taking up lodging in a one-time manor. Now, they were a religious sisterhood, living according to an ecclesiastically approved form of life, their home was a convent in which daily God came to them through the ministry of an alter-Christus whose special care they were, their number had increased, and—oh, very special blessing!—one of the little band had preceded them to the throne of God where they were confident her sisterly intercession never failed them.

Hardly had spring given way to summer when they received another token of Divine Providence. Bishop van Bommel came to the convent on the heath! With great kindness the prelate greeted Mother Magdalen, evincing a lively interest in all that she had to tell and show him. Later, addressing all the sisters assembled in the chapel, he spoke of Mother Magdalen's visits to Liége, and related how she had overcome his objections by her simple humility and trust. He congratulated them on having such a mother and professed himself well pleased at their progress and spirit. In his final words he urged them among other things to use their voices solely for the glory of God and to strive for true lowliness.

A few days after his Lordship's visit Mother Magdalen told the sisters she had received a letter from him and that it was his wish that the sisters should wear stockings. He also expressed the opinion that their religious garb would be much improved if the sisters would wear a white veil of some sort under the black one.

"That's easier said than done," came from Sister Frances. "Have you any ideas about it, Mother? Or does anyone?"

No one had but, as Sister Clara said, it didn't have to be done immediately. "Why don't we all think about it for a few days," she suggested, "and surely one of us will have a workable pattern?"

Mother Magdalen approved, and it wasn't long before a definite type of white veil was decided on, a shoulder length, wide piece of starched linen which gave the soft black veil a form and held it away from the face. Though it meant more work, as this added piece must be starched and ironed each week, the sisters agreed that the new headdress, while still simple, was far more attractive than the former. As Sister Anthony remarked in her droll way, it made the good-looking ones better-looking and it didn't hurt the others.

"Come in." Mother Magdalen raised her head from the account book as she responded to the vigorous knock at her door.

Sister Anthony entered with the customary greeting, "Praised be Jesus Christ," and as soon as the superior's "Now and for all eternity" had been said, she launched into her story.

"Mother, I told you last night, you remember, that there was only enough bread for breakfast, and now that it is over the bread is gone and all there is in the house is some coffee. What am I going to cook for dinner?"

"Don't look so worried, Sister," Mother Magdalen smiled at her cheerfully. "Perhaps one of our friends will stop in with something, or one of the pupils might pay her tuition today in the form of meat or vegetables. I just don't have any money now. As I told the sisters yesterday, I used every bit we had on hand to pay on the debt. But don't worry," she repeated. "You know that God will provide."

And of course He did! Just before dinner a couple of their old friends from the town brought them some freshly baked loaves and a large ball of cheese. Sister Anthony knew it would happen that way. She told Sister Frances about it that afternoon as they were doing the church wash. "You know it has happened several times since we've been here. I don't really worry any more when there's nothing to serve. I just tell Mother about it and she says, 'God will provide.' And He does. It always seems to me like a miracle."

Sister Frances reached for the pot of boiling water and carefully poured it into the tub before she spoke. "I don't suppose it's really a miracle, Sister, but it is certainly God's answer to our mother's wonderful trust and confidence in Him. Somehow, she just seems to *know* that He is going to take care of us. Remember the time Father van der Zandt wanted to unite us to that Franciscan community in Arendonck?"

"Yes," Sister Anthony nodded. "Mother didn't seem to be upset about it at all, did she?"

"She wasn't. And what's more," Sister Frances continued as she shook out an alb and looked it over critically before plunging it into the tub of water, "she even reproved me because I was worried! She had absolutely no doubt that the project would fail, as it did. Yes, Divine Providence surely does watch over us for we are getting along so well. Now, if only these tenants would move we could put in a garden and raise our own vegetables. That would help the food situation a lot, wouldn't it? And I bet you and I could do a lot with that smelly moat, too!"

Just then the bell rang for Office and the two sisters hastily removed their aprons and tidied themselves for this most loved of their spiritual exercises. Mother Magdalen called it the "service of the angels," and all the sisters remarked that she herself assisted at it with all the devotion and ardor of an angel.

Sister Frances hurried on so as not to be a second late. Tardiness at a spiritual exercise was one of the very few things that could bring a look of displeasure to the face of their kind mother.

Sister Gertrude walked more slowly as she was accustomed to meet Sister Clara at the foot of the stairs and assist her to mount them. It was becoming more difficult for the little sister to climb the stairs as rheumatism increased her lameness. Neither of these sisters could read as they had not had the opportunity to learn when they were young. Father van der Zandt had thought it best under those circumstances, not to make the Office obligatory for them as it was for the rest. However, they wanted to be one with the community in all things, so at the first sound of the bell, they, too, left whatever they were doing and proceeded to the chapel door. Here they knelt in the doorway, those two humble souls, and praised God and Mary as truly as did their sisters who were chanting the age-old psalms.

A few days after Sister Frances had expressed the wish that the tenants move, she got what she wanted. The three-year lease was nearly up, and as the people had found another place to live they left the Kreppel somewhat earlier than was expected. Such hubbub of excitement there was in the old place then! A veritable orgy of scrubbing and whitewashing began. Sisters Anthony and Frances joyfully left the inside work to the others while they took to themselves the herculean task of clearing and beautifying the large grounds. Their first concern was to get in a planting of vegetables against the coming winter. Day after day they dug, planted, watered and weeded this garden area so that it was some weeks before they could turn their attention to the rest of the property.

"It's going to take years!" Sister Anthony groaned, as they viewed all that had to be done.

"Well, then, the quicker we begin, the quicker we'll be finished," responded the irrepressible Sister Frances. "Let's ask Mother Magdalen to come over the grounds with us so that we can plan just what is to be done."

For several days Mother and the two sisters, aided by various bits of advice from the community, studied the condition and possibilities of the unkempt land. A spot at the remotest boundary of the property was selected for the cemetery; another section was to be added to the small orchard. Rough plans were made of the approximate position of walks, shrubbery and flower gardens.

"Be sure to save one nice spot for our little statue of St. Francis," directed Mother Magdalen. "Perhaps it will become a loved garden shrine in the years to come."

Sisters Anthony and Francis worked long hours each day, clearing the selected area of stones, stumps and rubble that had accumulated during the years of neglect. They had accomplished an enormous amount of the work by the time winter arrived making it impossible for them to continue.

Winter always brought with it an increase of discomfort and even a certain amount of downright suffering. With the exception of the chaplain's quarters and the kitchen, the rooms were unheated and the cold flagstone floors of the downstairs rooms resulted in many colds and severe attacks of rheumatism. As for food, though they never actually had nothing, they seldom had enough. Very little money came in as only a few of the children attended the school during the severe winter months. But the sisters were happy and cheerful.

In her talks to them Mother Magdalen would often insist on the value of the good intention and the spirit in which they should accept these hardships. "Let us rejoice," she would exhort them, her face glowing with her own strong spirit. "Let us rejoice when we have an occasion to practice the poverty we have vowed. With a joyful heart let us strive to be contented. Remember, the Kingdom of Heaven will be ours."

However, though she urged them to sacrifice and mortification, Mother Magdalen deeply sympathized with the sisters and she did what she could to alleviate their sufferings. For instance, since the price of coal was prohibitive, and it was impossible to have fires in the rooms, she obtained for each sister a little iron "firepot." This little pot, filled each morning with live charcoals banked with ashes, would last pretty well the whole day. They had flat tops so that whenever the sisters were seated they could put their feet on the lid and thus obtain some degree of comfort.

Winter lingered too long for Sister Frances, who ached to get to work on the moat. With the rocks and boulders from the land already cleared, she and Sister Anthony had filled up the dried parts of the moat and later they would get several loads of dirt for the top layers so that all the newly made land could be cultivated. The one section which contained the foul water they intended to clean out and drain, so that the water from the feeding spring could flow through fresh and clear as it must have done in former times. February brought a few deceptively mild days and the eager sister donned her outdoor working clothes.

"Just let me get started," she responded to Sister Anthony's remonstrances. "You needn't come out yet. I'll just work a couple of hours on these nice days and that will give us a good start for the spring." So for several days the young woman dug or lifted out masses of rubbish and rocks. Since the ground was frozen it was a difficult job, but it was the kind of work she loved, and so, one day, she didn't notice that the February thaw began to freeze with sudden thoroughness.

"I wonder where Sister Frances is." Sister Clara indicated the empty place next to her at recreation that day.

"Oh, she's working on the moat and perhaps she did not hear the bell," explained Sister Anthony.

"Will you call her, Sister?" Mother Magdalen asked with a worried look. "She really ought not to be out there. It has turned quite cold again."

Sister Angeline laughed. "Don't worry about her,, Mother. I don't think Sister Frances ever feels the cold, she works so hard."

Mother Magdalen said nothing but her thoughts went back

some years before to the winter nights when this same Sister Frances used to walk the street in front of the little house, stamping her feet and waving her arms in an effort to urge some heat through her cold body.

Running steps were heard in the hall and a moment later a distraught Sister Anthony appeared in the doorway. "I need help," she cried, "Sister Frances is frozen in the moat!"

The spell of shock held them immobile for a moment, then with cries of horror the sisters dropped their work and ran after Sister Anthony. Whitefaced, with the first feeling of fear she had ever experienced, Mother Magdalen stopped only long enough to prevent Sister Clara from following the others. Her heart filled with anxiety, for one loved companion still had thought for the welfare of another one.

As they hurried towards the moat with the terrifying words "frozen in the moat" still ringing in their ears, the sisters hardly knew what to expect. It was a relief to find that Sister was not so much frozen "in" the moat as "to" it! There she stood, a pathetic figure in the bitter cold, unable to move until some of the sisters had climbed down into the moat, dug around her feet, and pulled and tugged until the frozen ground gave up its prey.

Determined to clear at least one space on the bed of the ditch, Sister had not noticed that the water was slowly seeping up through the mud and rocks. She had to stand in the one small space as she hammered and pried the frozen rocks apart and her wooden clogs sank deeper and deeper into the softened earth and the sudden drop in temperature caused the shallow water around her feet and ankles to freeze into a tight trap. It was only when she attempted to climb out that she had discovered what had happened. Finding that she could not free herself she had called and called, but the wind had evidently carried the sound of her voice away from the house. Meanwhile, her clothes, which had been soaked with perspiration, had quickly frozen so that she seemed to be encased in ice.

Tenderly her sisters carried her, exhausted and shivering, into the convent. "The bake oven is still warm from the early afternoon, Mother," said young Sister Colette. "Can we put her in there until her clothes thaw out?" It was a novel idea, but it was done. It struck no one as being humorous at the time, but later, they all, especially the victim, had many a good laugh over the "baking" of Sister Frances!

"Go right up to bed now, Sister," said Mother when the poor sister had sufficiently thawed out. "Sister Anthony, please get something to wrap around her as she goes through the cold halls, and Sister Colette, will you see that two little fire-pots are well filled and put in her cell."

In no time at all the protesting Sister Frances was in bed and someone was handing her a cup of steaming coffee. The unaccustomed warmth and rest must have been just what she needed, for a slight cold was the only effect of an experience that could have had disastrous results.

One result there was, however, that was hard for her—she was forbidden to work out-of-doors again until spring had definitely come. Mother Magdalen was very serious as she imposed that prohibition.

"You really should not have been out there at all in this weather," she reproved. "It was an unwise thing to do. I know there is much work to be done, but it has waited this long and it can wait a little longer."

"But, Mother," the chastened sister pleaded, "it seems to me that I ought to do as much work as I can. You know I kept Our Lord waiting six months before I answered His call, and then, a few years ago, I nearly turned my back on Him because of cold and hunger and work. I just *have* to work harder and longer than the others to make up for my unfaithfulness."

Mother Magdalen's expression softened as she looked into

the earnest eyes, but she answered gravely, "You are thinking of Our Lord as a severe taskmaster. Sometimes, it is true, we have atonement to make, not, however, by *doing* more but by *loving* more." Her sudden, sweet smile broke through her gravity as she traced the sign of the cross on Sister Frances' forehead, saying, "Remember, always, child, that the good God is so very, very good!"

Father van der Zandt crossed the little bridge and looked down into the moat. The clear, limpid water sparkled up at him and he marveled again at this product of the sisters' labor. It was early spring, 1839, and barely a year had passed since the tenants had moved, leaving the whole of Kreppel and its grounds to the complete ownership of the sisters. In that short time the change in the once neglected property was astounding. Even this early he could see the promise of beauty in the newly planted shrubs and vines, the budding of the pruned trees, the tender grass, able for the first time in many years to push its shoots above the earth. Far down by the orchard, he could see Sisters Frances and Anthony with spades and hoes, and he knew that before the summer was over they would have accomplished more wonders. Indeed, these poor unlettered women were achieving wonders and results that professional landscapers and gardeners would have been proud of.

"It's now the children's playtime," the priest mused taking out his big silver watch. "I may as well go around to the playground as Mother Magdalen will probably be there."

As he turned the corner of the building, the little girls rushed toward him with squeals of delight and flung themselves upon him. They were never afraid of him, and indeed he gave them no cause to be. Stern and harsh as he often was, with the children he was never anything but kind. He was right,

Mother Magdalen was there. Though she was seldom in the schoolroom now that there were more capable teachers, she too loved the children and often spent the few minutes of recess with them.

"Good morning," Father van der Zandt called cheerily, thinking to himself that Sister Catherine, as he sometimes called her, was looking older and more tired lately. He wondered if she were ill, but when she drew nearer he noticed only the clear, expressive eyes and the sudden sweetness of her smile which never failed to astonish him, and he forgot to ask about her health.

"Good morning, Father," she said pleasantly. "Did you come to see the children?"

"No, I didn't. I came to see you." The priest untangled himself from the clinging hands and arms. "Run along to the schoolroom, little ones. I want to talk to Mother now. Let's just walk around to the front," he continued turning to Mother Magdalen, "What I have to say won't take long. It's about the chapel. Well, since we definitely decided that we need a larger chapel I've been giving the matter a lot of thought. You remember that we considered adapting the large barn?" She nodded. "However, I was talking to Sister Theresa about it yesterday—by the way, there's a woman with a head on her!— and she suggested building an entirely new chapel. The more I think about it, the better I like it. How about you?"

"I think it's a fine idea, Father," she answered instantly, "only, what will we use for money?"

Father van der Zandt glanced at her sharply. Was she perhaps referring to his own words to her when she first proposed buying the Kreppel? "What will you use for money? Apples? Eggs?" But no, she wasn't like that, he knew. Now, if it were Sister Frances——!

"You haven't any I know," he grimaced ruefully, "and it's going to take a lot. Luckily we have plenty of large trees on the grounds for the lumber, but labor will be high, not to mention the furnishings. Sister Theresa has a good idea of this, too. A begging tour, that's the way to raise money these days, and Sister has offered to do it herself."

He noticed Mother Magdalen's involuntary start and stopped abruptly. "What's the matter?"

The usually calm eyes raised to his were faintly troubled. "A begging tour, Father? And Sister Theresa? She is still a novice as you know."

Heavy eyebrows lowered at her and the all-too-familiar frown darkened the priest's face. "Masoeur," he said heavily, "Sister Theresa is a novice, it is true, but she is nearly thirty years of age, and she is quite familiar with the ways of the world, which you are not. And furthermore, what is wrong with a begging tour? Didn't St. Francis and his brothers beg? Are you too proud to follow the same course?"

That was unjust and he knew it. No one knew better than he, the depth and utter genuineness of her humility, but he was angry. "I have spoken to the Dean about it and he heartily approves of both the tour and Sister Theresa's offer. You will agree, I hope, that the Dean and I understand these matters better than you do!"

Mother Magdalen lowered her eyes for a moment. Dear God, how this man could hurt! "I am convinced, Father," she answered simply. "As you say, you do understand these affairs better than I. You are our director and it is for you to decide on such matters. Please forgive me."

Disarmed as he always was by her selflessness and a little ashamed of himself, he spoke kindly again. "Many of the restored Orders are begging now, Mother, with the approval of the authorities, so you need not worry about it not being the proper thing. Sister will beg only in Belgium where she knows many influential people and you will, of course, appoint a companion for her. Talk to Sister Theresa, Masoeur, and I'm sure you'll feel better about it."

"I'll do that, Father," she responded gravely, and as the priest crossed the bridge to his patiently waiting horse, she turned into the house and made her way to the chapel where she never failed to obtain help. When she left, some time later, she was fully resigned to what was of natural repugnance to her, and resolved to further as best she could the evident designs of God.

As the sisters completed the customary visit to the Blessed Sacrament after dinner, Mother Magdalen whispered to Sister Theresa, "Come to our room for a few minutes, please."

"Sister," the superior began without any preamble. "Father van der Zandt has told me about the begging trip and your offer to take part in it. Are you still of the same mind?"

"Oh yes, Mother," the young sister answered eagerly, "that is, if you approve, Mother. I told Father that."

"Tell me about these begging trips, Sister. I would like to know just what you are going to do and what results you can expect."

Sister Theresa explained to her superior just what would be involved in such a trip. Her first act would be to go to an influential family she knew very well and obtain a letter of recommendation which would introduce her to many other people of means. "Most Belgian Catholics are very generous, Mother, and they love the priests and sisters, so I am sure we will have a successful trip."

They talked over the project for several minutes and both agreed that Sister Angeline would be an excellent companion. Though she was no older than Sister Theresa in years, she had been longer in the convent and was a little more trained to the demands of religious life.

"We'll see Father van der Zandt tomorrow," Mother Magdalen concluded the discussion, "and tell him that you and

Sister Angeline will be ready whenever he wishes you to leave. Will you please tell Sister Angeline to come to me when she is free?"

As Sister Theresa smilingly closed the door behind her, Mother Magdalen's thoughts flew back to the day nearly two years ago, when the sister, then Petronella Rooyakers, had come to the convent on the heath to ask admission as a postulant. Though Mother Magdalen had never met the young woman, who was not of the district, she was at once captivated by the charming simplicity and deep sense of the spiritual displayed by this well-to-do woman of the world. It was a further joy to discover that Miss Rooyakers was well educated and so would be a definite asset to the school. Candidly, Mother Magdalen had placed before the would-be religious the hardships and deprivations that would be hers should she choose to join their struggling Franciscan family, but the girl accepted all calmly and wholeheartedly. It was just what she wanted, she assured the superior. They talked together a long time, this Mother and her new daughter, and the latter opened her heart freely to the one in whose hands she was placing her religious formation. Mother Magdalen recalled her own words to the community that afternoon as she told them about the prospective postulant. She had said, "Sisters, I have just accepted a young woman who knows how to confer with God and man."

Petronella had not disappointed her. She was a talented, capable person, a wonderful teacher. In fact, she was so successful in the classroom that several wealthy families of the surrounding towns had sent their children to be taught by the Heythuysen Franciscans. But these gifts, appreciated though they were, were as nothing to Mother Magdalen compared to the sister's qualities of character and soul. She was simple, direct, strong; her one aim was to have God's will fulfilled in her. She loved her Franciscan vocation intensely and was determined to live it to the full. All this Mother Magdalen knew, but she did not even suspect that it was her own perfect abandonment to Divine Providence, her own radiant Franciscan spirit, that beckoned the young sister forward along the path to sanctity.

Sister Angeline's forceful knock recalled her thoughts to the present and calling a "Come in" she prepared to tell the sister of her strange assignment. Sister Angeline's rather mannish appearance hid a shy though not timid character. She was a good, solid sister and accepted her superior's commission with her usual spirit of unquestioning obedience. It was a task to be done and she would do it well, but she had none of Sister Theresa's fire and zest for it.

"Why is it," Mother Magdalen asked herself that night as she sat in recreation with the sisters, "that I so often seem to have such startling announcements to make?" She smiled, knowing well how quickly the quiet, peaceful faces she was now looking at would change with her words. Putting down her knitting she said clearly, "Sisters, I have a little news for you." Now, what community is so retired and so mortified that it does not immediately prick up its collective ears at the word "news"? In convent parlance it connotes, not world-shaking events, but happenings intimately connected with the sisters and their affairs, so she had their immediate and undivided attention.

"According to the wish of our reverend pastor," she went on, "Sisters Angeline and Theresa will start in a few days, to conduct a begging tour through the districts of Belgium. The money thus raised will be used to finance our new chapel."

A begging tour! Reactions were instant and varied, the superior noted. Some faces mirrored dismay, as she knew her own had done that morning; on others she caught expressions of perplexity or disapproval, while on the faces of the younger sisters, shock and delight seemed to be vying with each other!

She knew how they felt, each one of them, from those who were afraid of such a return to the world, to those who could envision it as high adventure. That capability of hers to understand and feel with others was one of the things that made her so dear to her sisters.

For a few minutes she let the excitement bubble, then quieted them with a brief explanation of the project. She showed them the legitimacy of such a procedure and the responsibility, not only of those who were to take part in it, but of all of them to pray that all would go well. Poor Sisters Theresa and Angeline were the objects of a barrage of zealous envy, advice, warnings, and congratulations! They received it all with imperturbable good humor, in the spirit in which it was given, and went off to night prayer with the warm glow that came from the realization that others were interested in their affairs.

Father van der Zandt was in favor of a quick start, so within a very few days all arrangements were made and Sisters Angeline and Theresa were bidding goodbye to the sisters who accompanied them to the little bridge.

As the travelers knelt for Mother Magdalen's blessing, Sister Theresa looked up into the deep, clear eyes. "Don't worry, Mother," she whispered, "nothing will make us forget that we are religious!" The motherly face broke into a smile, "I am sure of it," she responded quickly, "very sure of it. Otherwise I could not have let you go."

Sister Ann came walking briskly across the heath. Usually after a day spent helping the sick in the village she was too tired to hurry, but walked slowly along, enjoying the fresh air and thinking loving thoughts of her sick poor in whose service Mother Magdalen had confidently placed her. Today, however, was different. As she neared the moat, Sister paused, looked around, and seeing that there was no one to be a witness to her movements she picked up her habit and raced across the bridge, into the convent, and up the narrow stairs to come to a sliding halt at the open door of the superior's room. Mother Magdalen looked up from her accounts, ready to administer a reproof to the violator of religious decorum, but the rebuke died before the shining eyes of the young sister. "Poor child," Mother thought to herself, "a good run was probably like a tonic to her."

Sister Ann was quick to catch the change of expression and she smiled happily. "Oh, Mother," she cried. "I just had to run to tell you that they'll be here for supper this evening."

"They," it turned out, were Sister Angeline and Sister Theresa. They were in one of the neighboring villages and Father van der Zandt had driven over to get them.

Quickly the glad news spread through the little community and preparations were made to welcome the travelers back to their convent home. Each one's cell was dusted and aired, and

Mother Magdalen herself filled and lighted their little firepots to take off the early spring chill. Sister Gertrude ransacked her slim store of provisions to find a special treat for the evening meal, and Sister Frances discovered a handful of curious little crocuses which had just put their little noses through the hard ground. These added a cheery note to the bare refectory table. Every service that could be thought of was performed, and the two weary sisters who climbed out of the pastor's wagon that evening found a welcome in which poverty had been hidden by love.

After-supper chores were speedily disposed of and the sisters gathered around the returnees, demanding to hear every last detail of their venture. Tellers were no less eager than listeners; indeed, they sometimes both talked at the same time but that only made the account more delightful. People had been so wonderfully kind to them; the amount collected had been far more than they had hoped for. Many of their experiences were amusing, some touching. "Now just look at that," good Sister Coletta interposed several times, "the really poor people are so generous!"

As the fascinating tales seemed never ending, Mother Magdalen brought the recreation to a close. "Let's save something for tomorrow," she suggested, "so these poor sisters can go to bed. They must be worn out, and Sister Theresa seems to be getting a cold."

As the sisters began to fold up their mending and wind up the yarn, one of the young sisters said impulsively, "Everybody you told us about was so good to you. Wasn't anyone mean or rough with you?"

Sister Theresa looked at Sister Angeline who returned her smile with a rueful grimace. "We did have one rather unpleasant experience," she acknowledged. "We'll tell you about it tomorrow."

Mother gave the sisters the signal to start to the chapel for night prayers. Quietly she motioned Sisters Angeline and Theresa aside and said softly, "Sisters, just say 'Good night' to Our Lord, and quickly get to bed. We're so happy to have you back with us."

As the superior hastened to catch up with the sisters, Sister Angeline whispered to her companion, "She's so understanding, isn't she? It's so good to be home in our poor little convent."

No sooner had the sign for recreation been given the next day after dinner than a chorus of voices demanded the "unpleasant experience."

"I'm afraid your expectations are too high," Sister Theresa laughed. "No one set the dogs on us or called the mayor. It was just, as I said, unpleasant."

"A little more than unpleasant, I think," put in Mother Magdalen, who had heard the story that morning. "It gave you the seeds of that cold you haven't been able to shake off!"

"We'll take care of that, Mother," promised Sister Anthony, who greatly missed her visits to the sick and was never so happy as when she had some one to "doctor."

Sister Theresa smiled her thanks and then launched into the story.

Late one evening, she and Sister Angeline had stopped at a lonely farmhouse to beg for a night's shelter. To their dismay, the elderly woman who answered their knock was very reluctant to let them in. She had called her husband, and he, too, had an air of hostility. The sisters explained what they were doing, and that there seemed to be no other farm in the vicinity and that it was getting dark. After a few minutes' conference with her husband the woman grudgingly admitted them to a small, dark parlor where she left them with such a look of suspicion that they would not have been surprised to hear her draw a bolt across the door! No refreshment was offered them and though they were hungry, having walked many miles since their last sandwich, they had judged it wise to let well enough alone. They had gratefully sat on the hard chairs to wait until the woman would return with a straw pallet and a blanket or two. They had said their night prayers and talked awhile before they finally realized that there was to be neither pallet nor blankets. Darkness had fallen and the March winds had risen; they had no light, no fire, and they were so tired.

Practical Sister Angeline met the situation squarely. "We can't sit on these chairs all night if we expect to sleep, and anyway, it's probably not much colder lying down than sitting up." She took off her big shawl, opened it out to its full size, wrapped herself in it snugly, and stretched out on the floor, using her little bundle as a pillow. "You'd better lie down, too," she said, looking up at Sister Theresa. "It's easier to rest this way."

Sister Theresa had been reluctant to sleep on the floor, not because of squeamishness, she assured her listeners, but because, though she had never been really ill, her constitution was not of the strongest. She had tried valiantly to compose herself more comfortably on the straight chair but it was impossible. Sleep tugged at her eyelids and it had become harder and harder to keep conscious enough to catch herself from falling. The chill of the room seemed to be increasing; she could hear Sister Angeline's rather ungentle breathing and knew that she was at least getting some measure of rest. With a sigh of defeat, her shawl tightly around her, Sister Theresa had finally laid herself down next to her companion, sure that she wouldn't sleep a wink. Suddenly it was morning, very early morning, and a shrewish voice was telling them it was time to be on their way. Stiff and sore, the sisters had smoothed their shawls and skirts as best they could, seeing that no facilities were to be offered them. With a few words of thanks and a promise of prayers they had left their unwilling hostess and gone out into the clear, crisp morning.

"So, as you see," concluded the narrator, "it wasn't really any more than unpleasant, and perhaps it wouldn't even deserve to be called that if it weren't for the fact that I can't seem to throw off the effects. Sister Angeline was fine after our brisk walk and a good breakfast at a very kind farmer's, but the stiffness and ache have stayed in my bones, and, as Mother noticed, the cold I contracted then has lingered."

"It was all my fault, too," burst from Sister Angeline as Sister Theresa finished.

The sisters gaped at her. "Your fault?" asked Sister Frances, "Why, how was it your fault?"

Sister Theresa tried to restrain her but she would not be silenced. "It was my fault because, from a few words I overheard, I know that farmer and his wife thought I was a man in disguise!"

Shrieks of horrified surprise greeted her announcement and she continued gloomily, "My feet and hands are so big—and that deep voice of mine—no wonder the old couple was scared!"

It was true. They all realized it as they looked at her in this new light. She really had a masculine appearance and, now that they thought about it, a rather mannish manner! Poor Sister Angeline! Any probable tactless comments were forestalled by Mother Magdalen's, "Don't worry about that, Sister. You have fine 'manly' virtues too, you know; courage, endurance, honesty, and I'm sure that Saint Francis is very happy to have you for his 'son'!"

Having thus eased the embarrassing moment, she went on, "Though we have been sympathizing with the sisters over this incident, I think perhaps we should rather be envying them!"

"How is that, Mother?" asked one of the younger nuns.

"Can any of you answer her?" Several shook their heads

and the others merely looked puzzled, so Mother Magdalen continued. "It is told in our Holy Father's life that one day some one asked him to explain that 'perfect joy' he was constantly talking about—"

"Oh, I think I know, Mother," interrupted Sister Frances, and at the superior's nod she continued. "I'm not sure of the exact words but St. Francis said something like this, 'If you're hungry and cold and you knock at a door and instead of letting you in, the people abuse you and call you names and say that you're impostors, then it's perfect joy.'"

Mother beamed approvingly. "That's it. Now Sisters Angeline and Theresa have had an experience not unlike that which St. Francis described. I'm sure that they did not in anyway show that unfriendly couple that they were insulted or hurt, and you know, they probably would never have told us about the incident if we hadn't been so persistent. They have had a little 'Franciscan experience' that has been denied to us, and that is why I say that in reality we should be envying them." This was quite a novel viewpoint to some of them and an animated discussion was soon going on with each giving her idea of perfect joy. Sister Anthony brought it to a close with peals of laughter when she remarked in her own inimitable way, "Well, if anyone in this community had perfect joy, I think it must be Sister Frances. Remember, she was not only frozen, but baked!"

Father van der Zandt wasted no time in getting the new chapel underway. With the funds collected by the sisters, men and equipment were hired and soon the exciting sounds of axes and saws, hammers and shovels, became the background music at the old Kreppel. Every day Mother and the sisters noted with joy even the smallest evidence of progress, eager for the first Holy Mass to be said in this their first real chapel. Many prayers went up that, when the building was completed, the Bishop would give permission for the Blessed Sacrament to be kept in its Tabernacle.

No one was happier about the chapel than Sister Theresa, but for awhile it looked as though she might never see the completion of the project in which she had had such a large share. Her cold, instead of clearing up, had settled in her chest; the soreness and ache in her bones had become definite pains and at last she was forced to go to bed in a high fever. In spite of loving care she grew worse and nothing seemed to give her any relief.

Father van der Zandt was alarmed; he had ambitions for this young sister, and now it seemed that death would bring an abrupt end to his plans. Mother Magdalen, too, was deeply concerned. She loved this daughter of hers, and the thought of losing one of those entrusted to her wrung her heart as it would any mother's. But she had great confidence that Sister Theresa had a special work to do and that God would spare her until it was accomplished. She comforted the sick sister with prayer and encouragement. "You must get well, dear Sister," she would say. "God wants you for His work, the community needs you and I depend upon you."

The pastor, however, was sure that Sister Theresa was dying. "I'm afraid she won't live to make her vows in June," he said to Mother one day. "I think she should make them now on what will probably be her deathbed. Don't you agree?"

"If you really wish it, Father, yes, but I do think you are worrying needlessly. She'll get better, I am sure."

But the priest was insistent. He still hadn't learned that Mother Magdalen never jumped to conclusions, nor made unfounded statements. "I'll tell you something else, Mother. We're not going to ask the community about it, either. You know they don't like her!"

"Don't like her?" cried Mother Magdalen, startled. "Father, we all think a great deal of Sister Theresa."

"Oh yes, you do, and maybe some of the younger ones, but the others don't. You know why?" he asked truculently. "Because she does needlework, teaches, makes lovely artificial flowers, instead of scrubbing, digging, cooking, and so on. They're good souls, those old companions of yours, but they've done so much manual work all their lives that they've forgotten, or never knew, that God and neighbor can be served in other ways!"

"Father, I hope, in fact I'm sure that you are mistaken. Perhaps there has been some reserve on the part of the sisters you speak of. They realize that Sister Theresa is well born, well educated, and they are neither. I think perhaps they may look upon her with a little awe, but not dislike, never dislike," Mother said firmly. "Sister Theresa has always been most confiding and open with me and she has never mentioned noticing anything untoward in the sisters' attitude toward her. Nor has any sister ever spoken to me of her, save in terms of admiration. Has Sister Theresa complained to you?"

"No, she hasn't," the priest admitted, "but I just feel I'm right and I'm not going to chance her Profession to their vote. I'll take the responsibility on myself and let her make her vows." And he did just that.

The little ceremony in the infirmary cell was beautiful, beautiful because of its very nature, but it was a little sad too, sad because what was done so privately should have been a community feast, a family joy. Mother Magdalen stayed at the bedside of the young sister after Father van der Zandt had left and for a few minutes spoke to her of the Vocation she had just sealed with her vows. "Now we will pray the Lord that He lets you stay with us so you can practice what you have just promised," she smilingly concluded.

Greatly to Father's surprise and everyone's joy, Sister Theresa suddenly took a turn for the better and regained her health and strength so quickly that she was able to pronounce her Vows publicly with the other sisters in June.

One morning toward the end of June, Mother Magdalen received a letter from the Bishop's House. At sight of the official crested envelope her heart stopped and then raced on wildly. Outwardly calm, she took the letter in both hands and holding it against her breast made her way to the little chapel, where after uniting her will with God's she opened the missive. It was short, very short. Before she had come to the end of it her face was alight with joy. "Thank You, Lord," she said aloud and looked lovingly at the Tabernacle where He would soon dwell! For the Bishop, entirely unsolicited, had written to say that the Franciscan Sisters under the superiorship of Mother Magdalen Daemen, were granted the privilege of having the Blessed Sacrament reserved in their chapel.

"See, my daughters," Mother Magdalen said to the sisters after reading them the letter, "how good is the good God! We intended to ask for this great privilege after the new chapel was completed but God has anticipated our desires so kindly that we are to have Him even in our poor little oratory chapel!"

All the sisters were intensely happy but their joy was nothing compared to that of little lame Anna Marie, Sister Clara. To her it was as if the gates of Heaven had opened. Four years of the cold and dampness of the Kreppel had added rheumatism to lameness, making walking so extremely difficult that she was unable to accompany the sisters on their visits to the village church. Now the Sacramental Presence would be so near, so near—just a few steps down the little hall!

"German, Austrian, French, Belgian, Dutch," chanted little Sister Marie, "what are we anyway, Mother?" When the laughter subsided Mother Magdalen stopped her spinning and turned to her youngest daughter, "I'll tell you what we are, Sister Marietje, we're Catholics! And religious! Dutch," she added softly. "But sisters, we owe a great deal to the brave little country of Belgium, and we must not forget that perhaps many of our neighbors, especially the children, may not consider themselves to be Belgian. It would be wise for us, therefore, to remember that we are first and foremost religious!"

Sister Marie's question was not wholly facetious. That morning when Father van der Zandt had come for his daily building inspection, he had brought the news that the Province of Limburg had been returned to Holland by the Belgian Government. Such a transfer had not been entirely unexpected since the King of Holland had finally recognized the independence of Belgium and had removed all Dutch soldiers from the borders.

Brave little Limburg had had a colorful history, as part of the Austrian-German Netherlands, then under the French. Later, after the union of North and South Netherlands, the flag of the House of Orange had flown over the Province, and, since 1830, Limburg had been a part of Belgium. No wonder some of the sisters thought it confusing!

"I don't suppose all this will make any difference to us here in the convent, will it?" Sister Anthony asked.

"I shouldn't think so," responded Sister Theresa, deftly twisting the petals of an artificial rose, "After all, there is religious freedom in Holland, and there are some strong Catholic centers."

Mother Magdalen's voice came, clear and placid, "Well, I'm afraid it will have some effect on us! Father has decided that Sister Theresa should again go on a collecting tour—this time through Holland!"

The reactions were varied. "What can he be thinking about!" sputtered Sister Anthony. "Why, she's barely out of her sick bed!"

Sister Angeline paled. "Not me, Mother, please, not me again!"

"Don't worry, Sister," the superior comforted, "We'll keep our 'son' at home this time."

"Did you know this, Sister Theresa?" some one asked, and Sister replied quietly, "Yes, Mother told me this morning after Father had gone." She turned to Sister Anthony. "Don't worry about me, Sister, I'm really well and strong." She smiled. "I've promised not to sleep on the floor again. Mother said that if we have any trouble we are to pay for our lodging the way we would do at an inn."

"Who is going with you?" The question came from young Sister Josephine, her face alight with interest. "Do you know? You don't! I wish Mother would choose me." This last was said softly, as if to herself.

"Who is going, Mother?" several queried.

"We haven't decided yet. You see, Father hasn't as yet had permission from the Bishop, though he is quite sure there will be no trouble about it. However, we'll wait until we hear, and then we'll look around for a suitable companion," and Mother seemed to smile directly at Sister Josephine.

Father van der Zandt was not too happy over the annexation of Limburg, but he realized that Holland might be a fertile field for the young congregation, and since with him to think was to act, he immediately arranged for an interview with Bishop Paredis, Vicar Apostolic of the Province. His Excellency was more than kind, giving not only his permission for the begging tour, but also a letter of introduction and approbation which the sisters were to present to the authorities in any district in which they wished to solicit.

The sisters' zeal was not less than their pastor's, and within a few days Sister Theresa and jubilant Sister Josephine were ready to leave. Every sister came out to bid them God-speed for this was to be a long good-bye. According to the itinerary sketched out for them by Father van der Zandt, they would be gone for seven or eight months!

"Just think," Sister Anna said, "when you come home the chapel will be finished!"

"Oh, I know, and I really hate to miss seeing it grow every day! But how wonderful it will be when we do come home!" Sister Theresa's eyes filled with tears. "I do hope some of you will write and tell us all the news. We'll be gone so long."

At this, Sister Josephine's eyes filled up, but an overflow was prevented by Father van der Zandt's, "All right. Get the good-byes over with. It's time." A loving blessing from their mother, an affectionate farewell from their sisters, and the travellers were off.

It was several weeks before the first letter came.

"We went first to the northern provinces of Groningen and Friesland," wrote Sister Theresa, "but they are so definitely Protestant that we soon realized nothing was to be gained there. Since we left the north we have come to several Catholic centers where the people are most kind to us."

Later on there were other letters, not long, but interesting and reassuring. "In many of the places there are monasteries of Franciscan Fathers. We always call on them and they direct us to the people who they know will help us. We really feel much more Franciscan since we have had so much contact with the Fathers." And at another time: "Bishop Paredis' letter is like an 'open sesame' for us. In every community a number of prominent Catholics make our cause their own. We are receiving help beyond all expectations. Your prayers are certainly bringing blessings to us. We are both well—no floors have been offered yet!"

Such letters were sources of great pleasure to Mother Magdalen and the sisters, but one day something far better than a letter arrived.

Little Sister Marie came all a-flutter to the superior's room to tell her that she had just shown two young ladies into the teachers' room which did duty as a parlor when necessary. "And I think they're going to enter, Mother! They met Sister Theresa and Sister Josephine and, well, why would they come all this way if they aren't going to enter?"

"Let's hope you're right, Sister Marietje. Our dear Lord knows we need sisters to do His work."

He did know and He was providing. The visitors proved, indeed, to be prospective postulants. Both had been deeply impressed with the charity, the cheerfulness, and the spirit of poverty evinced by Sisters Theresa and Josephine who had stayed in their town for some time. After a few talks with the sisters about their Order, its aims and spirits, and upon the advice of the Franciscan Fathers, the young women decided to ask for admission into the convent at Heythuysen. Any doubts they had in the matter completely vanished at their meeting with the foundress, and before that day was over the little Franciscan family was increased by two!

A glowing autumn gave way to an unusually mild December. "What perfect weather we have had all year," remarked Sister Frances to Mother Magdalen one day as they were sitting in the little out shed, peeling potatoes. "In fact," she continued, "it has been a wonderful year in every way, hasn't it? We renewed our vows for three years. Our Lord is here in the little oratory; our beautiful new chapel is almost finished; we've had several real nice gals enter! And," she added after a moment's pause, "we're not so hungry so often as we used to be!" She eyed the potato she was peeling and sighed, "They're nice, and people do give them to us, but I get so tired of potatoes!"

Mother Magdalen laughed heartily. "When you feel like that, my old 'Mary Catherine,' just think of the days and days when we never even saw a potato! That will cure you!" Sister Frances chuckled. She loved these moments with her Mother, and they were so rare. "When I have a little talk with Mother," she had confided to Sister Clara one day, "I always come away with a deeper love of God and my vocation even if we don't talk of anything holy."

Sister Clara had nodded understandingly. "I know, that's the way it is with me, too."

"Here, Mother," Sister Frances said now, "give me your basket and I'll take it to Sister Anthony. Be sure to put your shawl on when you go out, and God reward you for helping me."

"In eternity." Mother Magdalen gave the customary response as she folded her work apron. "In eternity," she repeated to herself. "That's it. What shall I wish to have done in eternity? I want to do what you want, Lord. Show me the way."

Draping the folded apron over her arm, and obediently wrapping the old shawl around her shoulders, she commenced her daily tour of the grounds. Automatically her eyes checked the garden, the moat, the children's playground, the new building, but her thoughts were on Sister Frances' remark, "a wonderful year." Yes, Sister was right. All the blessings she had listed had helped to make it so, but she had omitted to mention the greatest—the Community. Each member passed through the superior's mind, from the postulants, happy and eager in their new life, to the earnest novices and on to the professed, young and old. She doubted whether there was, anywhere, a group of women more devout and humble, or so zealously and determinedly in love with their vocation. Each one was dear to her beyond price, but there were some, who for one reason or another, seemed to shine a little brighter, such as novice Sister Marie. "Marietje" (little Marie) was always brimming over with happiness which found vent in gay and loving thoughtfulness for others. Already she had so endeared herself to the community that she was wholeheartedly nicknamed "Cause of Our Joy."

There was good Sister Anna whose heart was filled with love for the poor and sick and to whom God had given a remarkable understanding of the nursing arts, though she had had no training.

And Sister Theresa? A soul of sterling worth. One on whom, the superior knew without doubt, she could count to the utmost and who she felt would someday be of immense value to the little congregation.

Mother Magdalen's thoughts passed on to her oldest and dearest, the four companions of the early years. What did she not owe to them, her first daughters! God had been so good to give them to her, and to preserve them still to be her comfort. They were the salt of the Community, and, as Sister Frances had remarked, each one had again this year sealed herself to the Franciscan way of life. Yes, indeed, it was a wonderful year, and, yet—she was troubled.

It had all started the day Father van der Zandt had said, "Well, Mother, everything is going along fine now. I think this is a good time to start thinking about the boarding school."

She had agreed with him. From the first, a boarding school

had been included in her plans, and this did seem to be a favorable time. Sisters Theresa and Josephine were sending home financial help; more, they were making valuable contacts all through Holland, and people were being made aware of the Franciscan Sisters of Heythuysen. Without a doubt, many would welcome the opportunity to send their girls to a convent boarding school.

Not much was said about the project at that time, but at his next visit the priest had brought up the subject again. Together they chose a suitable part of the building, speculated upon necessary adjustments, furniture and the like. Not until he was ready to leave did the pastor let fall a remark that showed the trend of his thinking. "Of course, there's much more to opening a boarding school than one would think. We'll have to get prominent men to back us, and that will mean considerable contact with educators and other professional people."

She said nothing at the time, but after Father had left Mother wondered about that remark. Was he warning her by this little preview of things to come? At each succeeding conference about the projected school, Father van der Zandt's observations about the importance of "contact with the world," "educational standards," "influential patrons," "official recognition," and the like, became so pointed that at last Mother Magdalen could not fail to realize what he was obliquely suggesting. He wanted her to resign!

Since that moment of realization she had given much prayer and thought to the problem. Should she resign before her term of office had expired?

On the one hand, she not only saw but quite concurred with the priest's view. She was not, humanly speaking, the logical type of a person to carry on such an undertaking as the charge of a boarding school. Neither well-born nor well-educated, she had no important or influential connections. The ways of the world and its modern demands in education and social training were entirely unknown to her. No one knew her limitations better than herself. She was a nothing and a nobody. Surely, the school, the sisters, should be entrusted to a person of higher attainments.

On the other hand, she was superior by the Bishop's appointment, therefore her office was God-given. Did she have the right to withdraw, to turn over the responsibility to some one else? Then, too, she had founded sucessfully a religious congregation; God had chosen her for that work in spite of her weaknesses and defects.

She paused in her reflections and noticed that without realizing it she had completed the tour of the grounds and was at the front door. She had just time for a visit to the Blessed Sacrament before she went to help Sister Clara fold the wash.

As she knelt before the small Tabernacle which contained Infinity, her soul was inundated with a great calm—why, she had had the answer to her problem all the time! God would provide! How could she, even for a moment, have forgotten the truth by which she lived. "It only goes to show, dear Lord," she murmured, "what happens when I think myself important!" All her anxiety ceased. She would not withdraw. The term for which she was appointed would be up in a few months—God would take care of the matter then.

Neither she nor Father van der Zandt spoke of the termination of her office as superior, but both worked for it, each in a different way!

Prayer and sacrifice brought Mother Magdalen the firm conviction that her active part in God's design for the Community was completed and that the leadership would be put into other hands. She not only believed this, she hoped for it ardently. Her whole nature craved the solitude and retirement that had never been hers, and she fully trusted that God would give her some measure in her old age. She begged prayers of the sisters and prayed for this end herself, always, however, with loving submission to whatever He wanted of her. She was at peace.

Not so the priest. Over the many years of his association with Catherine Daemen, he had learned to appreciate her sterling character, and he realized that God had truly worked wonders through this poor farmer's daughter, but he also sincerely believed that her mission was ended. He saw no chance of success for the young congregation's exterior activities under her leadership. His zeal was tremendous—not so his confidence in God's Providence. He was afraid, in spite of Mother Magdalen's assurance, that the sisters would wish their beloved foundress to retain her office, and for that purpose would vote accordingly. To forestall this, he took matters into his own hands. The statutes of the congregation at that time permitted a direct interference by ecclesiastical authority at any election, and so Father van der Zandt hastened to his good friend, Dean Scheyven, and told him of his fears for the young congregation. "And who would you put in Mother Magdalen's place?" inquired the Dean.

"Sister Theresa Rooyakers," was the immediate answer. "Your Reverence has met her. She is able, influential and virtuous."

The Dean nodded. "The Bishop has heard of her, of course, through this collecting trip. What does Sister Theresa herself think of this move?"

Father van der Zandt was aghast. "Why, I've never even suggested it to her. But she will do as she is advised by authority, I am sure."

Gravely, the Dean agreed with the pastor that such a change might be highly advantageous to the sisters, and so it happened that Bishop Paredis, Vicar Apostolic of Limburg, received a letter from Father van der Zandt, parish priest of Heythuysen and spiritual director of the Franciscan Sisters of the same town. The letter requested, with a quite impressive list of reasons, that Sister Theresa Rooyakers be immediately appointed superior of the said sisters, replacing the present superior, Mother Magdalen Daemen.

The request was granted.

It was nearing the time for Sister Theresa and Sister Josephine to return from their long trip so Father van der Zandt wasted no time. He called at the convent, formally, and asked for Mother Magdalen to come to the little parlor. After a few words complimenting her on all she had done for the sisters, and dwelling on her need for rest and relief, he informed her that, without waiting for the elections, His Lordship had deemed it wise to appoint Sister Theresa as superior; the appointment to take effect immediately after the sisters' return.

The priest was conscious only that the face before him wore its habitual expression of peace and joy. He was in a hurry to be off, so with barely a word of caution about mentioning this to the other sisters, he left. He and the Dean had to hasten to Weert where they would meet Sister Theresa at the Franciscan monastery and break the news to her.

Mother Magdalen stood where he had left her. By the grace of God, she had been able to smile, but the humiliation had stung like a lash and for a moment the shame of it flooded over her and she felt such emotion as she had not thought herself capable of. "He couldn't even wait until God released me!" she said half-aloud. The words echoed back to her, "until God released me." Why, He *had* released her! This was the way He had done it! "What a poor creature I am," she whispered, looking at her crucifix, "I beg and plead for humility, then shrink when You send me a grace like this! Forgive me, Lord, and—thank You!" Later she could even smile at the incident. She had said He would arrange matters—and He did! The pain, of course, did not pass so quickly, but she offered it for the welfare of the congregation. Mindful of the pastor's exhortation, she confided the coming change to no one, but she prayed fervently for the sisters and most especially for poor, unsuspecting Theresa whose shoulders were young and delicate for such a heavy burden.

Dean Scheyven and Father van der Zandt accomplished their mission. As the latter had foretold, Sister Theresa accepted the appointment as the will of her Bishop, though not without tears and fears.

She and Sister Josephine were welcomed home joyously by the whole community, each of whom was startled to see Sister Theresa break into tears as Mother Magdalen greeted her. They wondered more, when they saw the superior put an arm around the weeping sister and lead her into the little office.

The installation ceremony was set for March 12 and at the appointed time the Dean, the pastor, and the Community assembled in the new chapel, where Dean Scheyven read the Bishop's letter aloud. Uneasily he cleared his throat. "Now, my dear Sisters," he began, nervously fingering the letter that he had just read to them, "you have all heard the Bishop's letter appointing Sister Theresa Rooyakers as your superior for a term of three years. I know you will accept this as the will of God and act accordingly. Sister Theresa, please come and sit here." He motioned to a chair before the Communion rail. Beside him stood Father van der Zandt, wiping his forehead and running his finger around the inside of his collar, thinking how hot it was in this cold house! He almost regretted the part he had played in this drama—Theresa now, there she sat looking as though she had cried for a week! And the sisters with their quiet impassive faces, except for one or two who were making no effort to restrain their tears. Thinking that it would make the installation easier he had broken the news to the sisters the night before, while Mother Magdalen had kept Sister Theresa busy over the account. But—he wiped his forehead again, and said in a voice made brusque through nervousness, "You may greet your new superior."

From her place in the back of the chapel Mother Magdalen rose quickly and advanced to the chair on which Mother Theresa sat. From force of habit the latter started to rise but Mother Magdalen restrained her by kneeling at her feet. She took the trembling young hands into her own, and they stayed like this a moment, the old mother who was now the child, and the young daughter who was now the mother, soul looking into soul. The new superior's face grew calm and the shadows lifted from her face as Mother Magdalen's voice rang out clearly, "Dear Mother Theresa, give me your blessing." When the inexperienced thumb had traced the sign of the cross lovingly and gratefully on her forehead, Mother Magdalen rose and, turning to the Community with a joyful face, said sweetly, "Come, my Sisters, and greet the Mother the good God has given us."

Dominated though she was by the redoubtable Father van der Zandt, Mother Theresa proved a capable and enterprising superior; she strove to preserve the spirit of poverty and simplicity which Mother Magdalen had instilled in the young congregation.

During her administration many improvements and advancements were made by the sisters. With the erection of a new wing and the training of teachers, the boarding school opened and flourished. The first branch convent was opened in Alkmar, far to the north; the first retreat for the sisters was held in the old Kreppel, now the rapidly growing Motherhouse; and the sisters adopted the Divine Office with its midnight chant.

God blessed the work of the young superior in a signal manner. Quite unexpectedly, the Bishop gave permission for Mother Theresa, Mother Magdalen and the older sisters to make their perpetual vows of poverty, chastity and obedience.

Though Mother Theresa continued her sentiments of love and affection for her old Mother in religion, nevertheless the first few years were not easy for Mother Magdalen. Nearly all of the sisters had been her daughters, bound to her by a tie stronger than blood; she had accepted them into the Order, guided them safely through the first bewildering period, taught them to live and love the spiritual life as exemplified in the Franciscan rule. She had been their mother, devoted and interested in all that concerned them. Now this tie was broken; the close association was a thing of the past. It had to be that way and she realized and accepted the fact long before the sisters did. Often they came to her for advice and comfort in misunderstandings or trials, but she never encouraged such confidences.

"I will pray for you," she would promise, "but that is all I can do. Speak to Mother Theresa about your trouble." Then, as later to her other superiors, she was always an example of complete loyalty. Toward the end of her term Mother Theresa completed a project very dear to all the sisters—the laying out of a new cemetery. This "God's Acre" was in one of the secluded lovely spots of the increasingly beautiful grounds, and all were justly proud of the achievement when it was consecrated on March 30.

When two weeks later the young Mother fell ill with a recurrence of the sickness she had had six years before, no one worried. But alas for Father van der Zandt's hopes and plans, before another week was out, Death, that respecter of no man's dreams, had taken Mother Theresa and she was laid to rest in her new little cemetery. She had greatly endeared herself to all the sisters by her motherly care for them, and they and Mother Magdalen grieved sincerely for her loss.

Without any interference from Father van der Zandt, the sisters chose Sister Bernardine as Mother Theresa's successor. She was young in religious life but virtuous and cultured, an experienced teacher and able administrator. What gave the sisters special confidence in her was her very deep love and veneration for the foundress, whose advice she often sought and on whose prayers and sacrifices she depended.

Hardly had the flowers begun to bloom on Mother Theresa's grave when it became evident that Sister Clara would soon be with her. Little, lame Anna Marie was dying. Her frail constitution could no longer withstand the hardships that life still entailed for the sisters—damp, unheated rooms, and lack of sufficient nourishing food. She was at peace, waiting quietly for her Lord to come. One day Mother Magdalen suggested to Sisters Anthony and Frances that they all go together to visit the invalid.

"It will give her such pleasure to have us all together again," she suggested with her usual thoughtfulness. How right she was! It was one of Sister's better days and though she could not talk too much she entered into the spirit of her friends, listened with all her heart and laughed at Sister Frances' merry sallies. What a wonderfully happy time they had, these four "originals." One memory led to another, some sad, some glad, and all cherished. As they rose to go at the end of the visit, Sister Clara put her hand restrainingly on Mother Magdalen's arm. "Wait a minute," she whispered, "I want to talk to you."

"Catherine," she said, unconsciously using the old name, "I am going to die soon, you know, and I want to thank you once more for taking me to be your companion. To you I owe my precious religious life. If you had turned me away, what would have become of me, a poor, ignorant cripple?" Her voice faltered. "You gave me the chance to live for God and I've done so little—so little."

Mother Magdalen knelt by the bed and took her friend's hands between her own, in the old familiar way.

"Now, little lame one, I'll tell you again why I accepted you. Because I needed you! God sent you to me because He knew I needed you—and He needed the love and service that only you, Anna Marie, Sister Clara, could give Him, and have given Him. Every step you've taken with that poor, twisted leg of yours has been for Him. Do you think He forgets those things? Oh, no, He is so good! And if there should be something lacking to you, remember, He will provide!"

This was the last conversation they had. A few days later,

lame Sister Clara was skipping joyfully up the steps of eternity!

For a few more years Mother Magdalen was able to do her share of the many tasks necessitated by the growing school and convent. Though she was glad to do anything, clean vegetables, wash dishes and do needlework, the assignment that gave her the greatest pleasure was to watch the little ones in their play time, or to help some backward learner with her catechism or number tables.

However, as she grew older, the weak constitution of her youth returned, aggravated by a severe case of rheumatism. Mother Bernardine wished to excuse her from all manual work but she begged to be given some charge. So, painfully her stiff fingers were forced to fold the children's wash, or to set the refectory tables for the sisters' meals, little, insignificant tasks that were important to her because through them she was serving others.

Faithful to work, she was equally faithful to recreation. She loved to be with her sisters and enjoyed every minute of the time they spent together. Good listeners are highly appreciated in every walk of life, and she was one of the best, though she often enlivened the conversation with her own dry humor. Mother Bernardine insisted that she spend some time out-of-doors whenever possible, a permission for which Mother Magdalen was very grateful. Trees, grass, flowers, birds, and water—all these had been a part of her childhood and she had never ceased to find delight in them. If her walks were solitary she would spend much time in the little cemetery where she knew that before many more years had passed she, too, would be resting. St. Francis in his wall shrine received his measure of devotion also. Sometimes the little ones were out for recess, and catching sight of her would come running, pinafores and braids flying, to throw their arms around her or to be the first to catch hold of her hands. On occasion, by dint of much coaxing and promise of extra prayers, they succeeded in persuading her to stay with them awhile. Smiling happily into their eager little faces, Mother Magdalen would tell them stories of their big sisters, or even their mamas she had taught so long ago.

On recreation days one or more of the sisters would join her little expeditions. They would stop at the moat, whose beautiful limpid water reflected the brilliant sky overhead and the roses that bordered both sides of the channel. Naturally, they would recall the time Sister Frances was frozen to the ground and had to be thawed out in the bake oven! Often Mother Magdalen would gaze at the imposing new wings and buildings that had gone up with the passing years. "It's beautiful," she would remark to her companion. "Thank God for all His goodness—but, oh, it is going to be much more beautiful before the plan is complete."

One would be hard pressed to point to any one virtue as outstanding in Mother Magdalen. Charity, humility, obedience, fidelity, mortification—she excelled in all of them, and they, together with the "little" virtues of thoughtfulness, graciousness, dignity, combined in her to make a perfect religious.

Young Sister Crescentia one day determined to watch all the older sisters very carefully for a period of time, to see if she could discover any faults in them. A presumption on her part for which she was later ashamed! She confessed to the sisters that though she had detected failures in each one of them, she could find nothing at all to criticize in Mother Magdalen. In her, the rule and customs were exemplified. Such religious fidelity, with its necessarily attendant mortification and control, sometimes makes for coldness or severity, but in Mother Magdalen virtue was always natural and attractive. Custody of the senses in no way interfered with her motherly interest in the sisters and all that concerned them. Now that she was older and the circumstances of earlier years no longer existed, she did not hesitate to comfort and advise when she saw a sister struggling under temptation or discouragement.

Several times she noticed that Sister Celestine, one of the younger sisters, bore the look of one undergoing a severe trial. Each day the shadows deepened under the troubled eyes, and the mouth that should have been curved with smiles was drawn and tight. One day, as the novice passed her, Mother Magdalen drew her over into a doorway. Putting her hand kindly on the young one's shoulder she said softly, "Take courage, dear sister, and trust in Divine Providence. This trial will pass. God wants you here." With another friendly pat, she went on her way leaving behind her a suddenly light-hearted young woman, who ever after declared that she owed the grace of perseverance to Mother Magdalen's prayers.

As a mother follows with loving care the fortunes of her children who have left her to establish homes of their own, so did Mother Magdalen keep in her thoughts and prayers the many foundations made by the sisters in Holland and Germany. And in this matter, as in so many others, she seemed to have special foreknowledge. No matter how difficult were the circumstances attending some of the foundations, if Mother Magdalen approved of the venture, Mother Bernardine and even Father van der Zandt would rest content, knowing that the enterprise would succeed.

Mother Bernardine often recalled the foundation she made in the first year of her superiorship. Syberkarspel, in the north, gave promise of being an ideal situation. The opportunity was too wonderful to pass up and Father van der Zandt, highly in favor of it, urged Mother Bernardine to send at least three sisters to open the new school and convent. When the superior delightedly told the community of the new branch house, she noticed uneasily that Mother Magdalen did not seem to share in the enthusiasm of the other sisters. However, the foundation was made and the first reports were glowing. Deep in preparations for new establishments, Mother Bernardine quite forgot her momentary doubt about her first settlement until one day Mother Magdalen came to the office with a strange message.

"Reverend Mother, I think you should make a visit to Syberkarspel at once; the sisters are in need of you." She made no further explanation, but putting aside all else, Mother Bernardine immediately made the journey to the north without any notification of her intentions. Such conditions as she found there convinced her that she had made a mistake in sending her sisters, and though her action caused a great deal of unpleasantness she withdrew them at once.

After that unfortunate experience, Mother Bernardine was careful to discover Mother Magdalen's reaction to any proposed foundation!

At one time, back in the early days at the Kreppel, Father van der Zandt had tried to affiliate Mother Magdalen's daughters with another Franciscan community. Nothing had come of it, of course; God had chosen Catherine to raise up a new religious family to serve Him with its distinctive form and spirit. Now, these same daughters were being asked to incorporate with their community a small newly formed group of Third Order Franciscans! The appeal for affiliation came from the members themselves. The story behind the request was an exceedingly interesting one. Briefly, Mother Angela van Cordier, through a strange sequence of events, had become owner of the lovely island of Nonnenwert in the Rhine, head of the school she established there, and a novice with the Ursulines she brought to the island. Finally, on the withdrawal of the professed Ursulines, she, with the two or three fellow novices, obtained permission from the Bishop to live according to the rule of the Third Order of St. Francis. Mother Angela felt no call to found a congregation. On the contrary, she earnestly desired to become part of an older, established branch of the Franciscans.

Fortunately, her director, Father Xaverius, was acquainted with the sisters of Heythuysen and he told Mother Angela somewhat of the spirit and work of this Dutch congregation whose foundress was still living. Mother Angela liked what she heard and immediately wrote to Mother Bernardine stating her position, circumstances and the desires of herself and her companions.

Mother Bernardine, as a matter of course, took the letter to Mother Magdalen. "Please read this, Sister," she asked, "and tell me what you think."

Mother Magdalen read it thoughtfully. "This letter was written by a beautiful soul, Reverend Mother, a strong soul, one that seems to have already grasped not only the principles of religious life, but the very essence of Franciscanism."

"Do you think, then," pursued the superior, "that we should accept her proposal? It would be quite an exception to allow these sisters to make their novitiate at their own place in Nonnenwert, as they wish."

Mother Magdalen paused a moment before replying. "I do feel that such is the will of God. Naturally, you would send some of our own to guide and train them in our manner of life, and they could come here for a period before making the vows. But such an important affair requires much prayer and thought, and, I would say, further knowledge of Mother Angela herself. Reverend Mother, why don't you go to this island of Nonnenwert and see for yourself?"

"You're right, dear Sister. Yes, I'll do that. Perhaps after the New Year I'll be able to get away. God reward you for your help, Sister."

But the new year brought a press of other business so that Mother Bernardine was forced to write to Mother Angela regretfully postponing her visit. "Perhaps this summer I shall be able to make it," she concluded, "but I cannot say definitely at this time. Meanwhile, let us redouble our prayers for light in this important matter."

Mother Angela was deeply disappointed. Summer! And maybe not even then! Perhaps they should try another congregation; there were some right in Germany, she knew. And yet—she felt such a deep attraction to the Heythuysen Franciscans, an attraction that had been strengthened by the story of Mother Magdalen, told by Mother Bernardine in their interchange of letters. Urged by her companions, she resolved to go to Heythuysen in hopes that the visit would either confirm her intention to become a part of this Order, were she received, or to look elsewhere.

Mother Angela immediately wrote Mother Bernardine of her intention and the purpose of her visit. "Please do not tell Mother Magdalen that I am coming," she asked. "I would like to have her quite unprepared. In that way I will feel sure that whatever inspiration I receive at this meeting will be the one for me to follow."

Her wish was respected. When, one evening, Mother Magdalen called, "Come in, Sister," in response to a knock at her door, she was quite unprepared to have a beautiful young stranger enter!

On her part, Mother Angela was surprised at the sight that met her eyes. A small, bare cell containing a straw pallet, a chest of drawers, a crucifix, and a combination prie-dieu and chair, in which sat an old sister with a face of heavenly peace. She noted the still and swollen fingers holding the rough beads of a handmade rosary, the neatly darned and patched veil. This was the foundress! This poor, simple woman! She moved forward quickly to prevent Mother Magdalen from rising to greet her.

"I am Angela von Cordier of Nonnenwert," she said simply. "I have come to talk with you, Mother Magdalen, if you have time for me." Since there was no other chair in the room she sat on the edge of the hard little bed.

No one was ever told what passed between the two women, so different in most things, so alike in the one thing that counts—devotion to God's will. But when Mother Angela returned to her island she greeted the eager waiters with the words, "I have met a saint—and all that I have desired and sought for in religious life I found at Huythuysen. God has provided, my Sisters."

"Good afternoon, *Mijnheer*," the Reverend Mother Bernardine greeted the artist who stood before his easel in the Community parlor as she and Mother Magdalen entered the room. "I have just told Sister that this is the last day she will be asked to come here as you expect to finish your work today."

She turned to the sister at her side, "God reward you, dear Sister, for all the time you have spent here with *Mijnheer* Jansen. I know that without your help we could not have had this painting done," and an odd little smile flashed between the superior and the artist. Had they looked at Mother Magdalen they would have been surprised to detect an amused smile tugging at her lips, but Mother Bernardine left immediately and *Mijnheer* turned to his canvas.

Mother Magdalen went to her customary chair by the window, placed her prayer book on the little table, and soon the rough brown beads of her big rosary were passing through fingers stiff and awkward with rheumatism. There was no sound in the room save the faint rattle of the beads as they counted her loving prayers and the soft swish of a brush moving over canvas. Just as she raised the crucifix to her lips in the last prayer, the artist spoke.

"Sister Magdalen." Courteously she turned a little so as to face him, and though he looked at her he said nothing for a moment until he had made a few strokes with his brush.

She was familiar with that routine by now! He looked again and gave a grunt of satisfaction. "I just wanted to tell you, Sister, that another half hour will see this finished. Do you mind staying a little longer?"

"Not at all, *Mijnheer*. I do hope your picture will be a success. Are you pleased with it?"

It was the first time she had mentioned his work, he thought. Heavens! Was she hinting to see it? Hesitantly he said, "Why yes, Sister. I think it is quite good. Of course, it would probably not interest you—you don't care to see it, do you?"

His reluctance was so evident that she had to smile. "No, thank you. I am really no judge of art at all," and she turned away quickly so that he should not see the twinkle in her eye at his evident relief. Poor man! She mustn't let him know that she had guessed what everyone from Reverend Mother down to himself was trying to keep from her!

Her thoughts went back to the day a few weeks ago when Reverend Mother Bernardine had come to her cell with an odd request. The sisters had hired a rather famous artist from Alkmar to do a painting for them. "*Mijnheer* Jansen," Mother had said, "wishes to do his work in the front parlor. You know there is such a good light from all those windows. We don't like to have him alone all that time, so, would you, dear Sister, sit in there while he is working? He will not disturb you and you will be free to read or pray as you wish."

"Certainly, Reverend Mother," she had responded, happy to be of some service to the community. She had not asked the subject of the picture but it had struck her that a convent sitting room surely offered limited scope to an artist!

Mother Bernardine had accompanied her to the parlor and made the introductions. *Mijnheer* Jansen had been very cordial, "Do sit here, Sister Magdalen," he had insisted, as he placed an armchair by one of the front windows. "From here you have a lovely view of your truly beautiful grounds," and thoughtfully he had moved a small table within her reach so that she would not have to hold her books in her lap. As she had gratefully accepted his attentions she had noticed his easel was by another window with its back toward her in such a position that the artist would almost be facing her while he was painting. Once or twice during the morning he had spoken to her, necessitating a small turn of her face towards him and he had glanced at her quickly, almost covertly. When he was ready to leave he had covered the canvas before escorting her to the door.

The same procedure had been followed each day. Now, she smiled again to herself, thinking of those days. "Dear Lord, they must think me even more stupid than I am," she murmured. Indeed, how slow would she have to be, not to become aware that *Mijnheer* Jansen was painting her own portrait! The realization was somewhat of a shock to her but it did not disturb her humility as it would have done some years before. She understood now that such things mattered not at all; if her superior and sisters wished her picture she would not thwart their desire. Their pleasure over the seeming success of their schemes amused her intensely. Day after day she went to the rendezvous in apparent ignorance, too kind and understanding to unmask their pious fraud!

It was a mystery to her why they would want her picture. She had been their Mother such a short while; it was so long ago; she had accomplished so little.

Deliberately pushing aside all thoughts of herself and the past, she reached over to the little table and picked up her prayer book. It was her Third Order Manual, her faithful companion since the days she was a Tertiary in Maeseyck. Her swollen, painful fingers found it heavy now; its leather was scuffed and scarred and the pages discolored with constant use. "It's like myself," she mused, "old and worn. Surely we can't last much longer." Lovingly she turned the familiar pages, pausing for a moment at the picture of Margaret of Cortona, the sinner-saint who had inspired her to take the name "Magdalen." After her conversion from a wayward life, Margaret had become a member of the Third Order of St. Francis, and her penitent love was so like a burning flame that she became known as the "seraphic Magdalen." Mother Magdalen lingered over the psalms and finally came to her favorite litanies. By now, all thoughts of the artist and his work were far away, she was busy about *her* work, the great work of intercession for her sisters, the Church, the needy.

When *Mijnheer* Jansen finally laid down his brushes, covered his picture and escorted her to the door, where he thanked her profusely for her company, she had already put the portrait out of her mind.

With each succeeding year Mother Magdalen's disability increased. Dropsy and a weak heart made it impossible for her to take a share in even the lighter tasks. Though she felt the loss of her physical powers keenly, she wasted no regrets over what she could not do, but concentrated on what she could do. The world needed prayer and sacrifice; her sisters needed love and kindness; she gave all, unstintingly. Literally, she prayed always but she never lacked time for the cheering word, the encouraging smile. From the oldest to the youngest the sisters knew they had in her a powerful friend, and they felt free to approach her at any time with their problems. She knew and understood very well the truth Tennyson would not immortalize until years after her time: "More things are wrought by prayer than this world dreams of."

The needs of the world were multitudinous and she prayed for them all in general. In particular she stormed heaven for missionaries, for the return of the Faith to Holland and to England, "Mary's dowry." How ardent were her prayers for the Holy Father, for priests, especially for those who had fallen by the wayside. These poor "shepherds in the mist" were the constant object of her intercession and no pain or sacrifice was too much if only she might move the Holy Spirit to dispel that mist with the light of His Grace.

But, above all, her prayer was for her daughters in Christ. Though the government of the sisters had long been out of her hands, there was no power in heaven or earth that could release her from the responsibility she owed to them. She had been chosen to bring the congregation to birth and it was still her obligation to do all in her power to foster the religious life of each member in particular, not only those whom she knew but also those who in future ages would belong to her family.

Her apostleship, all embracing as it was, enveloped her dear villagers, too. So confident were they in the potency of her intercession that it is safe to say that no project was undertaken without the warm sincerity of her "Yes, indeed, I'll pray for you. Don't worry. God will provide." No one who had recourse to her left her uncomforted or unencouraged.

Mother Magdalen one time confided to some of the older sisters that she begged God never to permit any external sign of His great favors to her. He did not always see fit to grant this request.

Often when she was visiting with some of the good people of the village a strange occurrence would take place. In the midst of her conversation Sister would suddenly cease speaking. Her attitude became one of listening; a shining radiance seemed to surround her whole being; her eyes, fixed on a far point, beamed with heavenly joy. As quickly as it had come, the ecstasy would fade and Mother Magdalen would calmly resume the conversation precisely where she had broken it off.

These momentary seizures of love were common knowledge, but there were manifestations of a higher degree witnessed only by a few of her sisters.

One day Sister Coletta, who was portress at the time, went

[175]

to call Mother Magdalen to the parlor but not finding her in her cell she went immediately to the chapel. As she reached for the holy water and turned to face the altar she barely stifled a scream—there indeed was Mother Magdalen—arms outstretched, face turned upwards, and her whole body, raised from the floor, was suspended in the air as though taking flight to heaven! Poor Sister Coletta fled trembling to the chaplain to tell him of the strange sight she had come upon.

"I'm not surprised, Sister," Father Cantors said after he had heard the account. "Mother Magdalen is a very saintly person, you know. But a word of caution, don't mention this to anyone else while she is living. It distresses her exceedingly to have such great graces known to others."

The gift of enlightenment and foreknowledge that had so often played a part in her life was not withdrawn in her last years. Shortly before Mother Bernardine was to leave on a visit to some of the branch houses, she received word that a priest friend of hers was in trouble so serious that he had been forced to leave his parish and take refuge in a Trappist monastery. Upset and worried, Mother Bernardine went to say good-bye to Mother Magdalen and obtain her help.

"Oh, Sister, I've just had dreadful news. Will you pray very hard for a very special intention?" That was all, no slightest inkling as to what the intention was.

"Certainly, Reverend Mother." The promise was given and no questions asked. "Don't worry too much. Perhaps you will have good news when you come home."

Weeks later when Mother Bernardine did return, she went almost immediately to visit a little with Mother Magdalen. She reminded her of the promised prayers. "I prayed for your friend, Reverend Mother," was the smiling assurance. "You need not worry; he is truly a holy priest, entirely guiltless in the matter with which he is charged."

Mother Bernardine was astounded. She had mentioned the

affair to no one at all, neither here nor in the convents she had just visited. As far as she knew, not one of the sisters had even heard of this priest or his trouble. A few days later she received a letter from the Trappist abbot in which he informed her of the unexpected death of her friend, and concluded, "He died a very holy death, and we here thank God for sending us this exemplary priest."

Mother Bernardine thanked God, not only for the innocence of her friend, but for His evident love of their first Mother.

About the same time, in another instance, Mother Magdalen was again God's agent in bringing comfort to the distressed. Young Sister Theatildis was ill. No hope was held for her recovery, and though she was quite resigned to die, she was, understandably, a little afraid.

"Do pray for me," she whispered to Mother Magdalen who had dragged herself to the infirmary to comfort the young soul. "Do pray that I die well."

"You are not going to die yet, child. In fact," the foundress laughed, "you are going to live to be an older woman than I am! You have a great deal of work to do before God calls you."

In utter trust Sister Theatildis accepted Mother Magdalen's words as prophetic and ceased worrying. She recovered fully, served the Order for many years as superior and novice mistress, and finally died in her eighty-first year!

There were many, many instances of this type and though Mother Magdalen could neither ignore them, nor be ungrateful for these heavenly favors, of themselves they meant nothing to her. She knew well they were no integral part of sanctity. Sometimes these favors resulted in humiliations for her, and not only humiliation but, in some cases, deprivation. Whether to test her spirit or to counteract any feeling of pride, the chaplain occasionally took it upon himself to mortify her.

Several times he passed her by at the Communion rail! Eyes closed, face lifted expectantly for the kiss of her Beloved, she would hear Him borne past her by the action of the priest! Slowly she would lower her head, and rising slowly, walk calmly but lonely to her pew. When others sympathized with her over this harsh treatment her only comment was: "He is the dispenser of the Sacraments, and he has the right to deny me Holy Communion if he judges it expedient."

Virtues are not isolated one from another in the saints. They are, as it were, interwoven, each one strengthening the others; but as in a beautiful, harmonious work one or more details stand out, so it is in the pattern of sanctity. Humility and confidence were Mother Magdalen's dominant virtues. Implanted in her early by parents of solid piety, they were strengthened and spiritualized by the ridicule, the censure, and the constant disappointments she met in carrying out the work for which she had been chosen.

It is probably in the so-called "little" virtues that saintly people differ so noticeably. Mother Magdalen's big "little" virtue was courtesy. Not that courtesy by which we understand the shallow, superficial amenities of society, but that of which a brilliant Catholic author has said, ". . . it seems to me, that the Grace of God is in courtesy."

What else but the grace of God could account for the fact that this woman, who was poorly educated; whose associates for many years were peasants and laborers; who had but for a short period of her life lived beyond the confines of a village, sensed a true courtesy possessed by few women of culture and refinement? In her, courtesy was tact but not dissimulation; kindness but not weakness; appreciation but not flattery. In a word, it was a spontaneous thoughtfulness of others, springing from her love of Christ.

A true Franciscan, Mother Magdalen found joy in many things, great and small. One can imagine the ineffable gladness that filled her soul when in 1852 her congregation was approved by Pope Pius IX. The seal of the Church was the seal of God.

As a baby, fresh from the baptismal font, the little Mary Catherine had been consecrated to the Blessed Virgin. As she grew so did her love for this heavenly Mother, and in all the trials of her life it was to that dear Mother that she turned for guidance and counsel. The proclamation of the Dogma of the Immaculate Conception was a great joy to her and when, later on, the news of Bernadette and the Lady set the world astir, it seemed to her that life could hold no further bliss!

But little things, earthly things, gave her joy, too; the song of the birds; trees rustling in the wind; the shy good-morning of a child. Every small success of her sisters, each young aspirant to the religious life, an added field of activity, the founding of a new convent; all these gave her such delight and joy that "God is so good, so very, very good" was almost constantly on her lips.

Mother Magdalen was greatly interested in all the branch houses but the one that seemed to give her the most pleasure, for some unknown reason, was Saint Catherine's Convent at Almelo. This was the seventeenth foundation made, and it was in April, 1858.

Shortly after this seventeenth convent was founded and the news of it had spread to the village, Mrs. Raetson, the mayor's wife, called on Mother Celestine, the local superior. During the course of their conversation Mrs. Raetson related how her husband had taken Mother Magdalen, then Catherine Daemen, all around the countryside looking for a new home and how they had found the Kreppel, now the beautiful Motherhouse.

"You know, Mother," the lady said thoughtfully, "this was the very first foundation made from the little house that Catherine and her companions built, and the convent you opened just lately is the seventeenth. You know what that means, of course, and if Mother Magdalen is well enough I'd like to see her now as it may be for the last time."

Mother Celestine was bewildered. "Of course you may see her, but I don't understand what you are talking about."

"You mean you don't realize that Mother Magdalen is going to die soon?" asked the good lady incredulously.

"Oh dear," Mother Celestine thought, "poor Mrs. Raetson must be ill!" Aloud she said kindly and patiently, "I'm afraid I really don't know what you are talking about. Mother Magdalen is far from well but she is not in any immediate danger of death. Anyway, what has that to do with the seventeenth convent?"

"It seems almost unbelievable that you haven't heard of Catherine's prophecy! I'm sure most of us older ones in the village know it," and the scandalized woman went on to enlighten the puzzled superior.

"Well, Mother, it was long before your time, of course, but you surely know about the little convent that Catherine, Anna Marie, Mary Catherine and Gertrude built down in the village?"

"Yes, of course. We have often seen our first little house and our dear old pioneers love to tell how they built it and of the years they spent there in the village."

"And well they have a right to," Mrs. Raetson nodded vigorously. "When I think of how those poor souls lived, and of all they did for us! Well, one day while the building was going on I stopped to help and chat a little. I remember very distinctly that Anna Marie (Sister Clara that was. You remember her?) was all tired out, poor little lame thing, and she was worried. She said something to Catherine to the effect that she didn't see how Catherine could sleep with a building project hanging over her head, and that it might come to nothing. Catherine said, now mark you, Mother, this is just what she said as Sister Anthony can tell you: 'Don't worry, Anna Marie, from this little house seventeen others will come before I die!' So there, that's why I want to visit with my old friend again. It might be any day now that she'll slip off to heaven."

"Yes, I see." The superior was thoughtful. "I'll call Mother Magdalen, Mrs. Raetson. Perhaps you'd like to take her outside. She loves it there but since her heart is so weak we don't like to have her out alone. And, thank you for telling me about the prophecy."

Mother Celestine assisted Mother Magdalen down the stairs and then went to the kitchen where she knew she would find Sister Anthony.

"Sister, Mrs. Raetson is here and she told me a remarkable tale," and the superior repeated what the mayor's wife had just told her. "Do you remember that incident, Sister? Did you hear Mother Magdalen make that prediction concerning the seventeenth convent?"

Sister Anthony was stunned. "Why, Mother, yes. I remember it very clearly and I'm sure Sister Frances does too. Why did I never think of it? Why didn't I ever tell you or Mother Bernardine about it? Stupid that I am! And now the seventeenth convent has been founded!" And strong, reserved Sister Anthony began to cry.

Unobtrusively, but with unremitting zeal, Mother Magalen was more carefully watched than ever, but she seemed as usual. Every spiritual exercise found her in prompt attendance, even the midnight office from which she had never been absent since its inception. She was just as thoughtful of others, just as interested in all that concerned the sisters, and as ready to smile or laugh.

Spring had blossomed into summer, when suddenly what all feared happened. Hardly able to drag herself from the chapel back to her cell, one day, Mother Magdalen felt so ill and weak that she consented to see the doctor. After a thorough examination, he gave his verdict tersely: Death at any moment!

The patient was silent a minute, then with a smile and a "God reward you, Doctor," she turned to Mother Celestine who was hovering anxiously near.

"Mother, since I am in danger of death, may I, for the love of God, receive the Sacrament of Extreme Unction?"

Father Cantors was immediately consulted with the result that when the sisters assembled in the choir for Vespers, they found Mother Magdalen there in her chair which had been placed in the center aisle. Quickly the word spread that she was to be anointed and that all would be privileged to assist at the ceremony.

From the moment Father offered her the Crucifix to kiss, Mother Magdalen forgot everything except the marvelous effects being wrought in her soul through this wonderful sacrament. In a low, clear voice she answered the responses and joined the community in the Penitential Psalms they offered for her intention. As the priest anointed each of her members she prayed, too, with all her heart, "Through this holy anointing and Thy most tender mercy, O Lord, forgive the sins I have committed through my senses."

"Look at her," one of the sisters whispered to her neighbor, "she looks like a saint."

"She is a saint!" came the vehement reply.

When the priest left the choir Mother Magdalen took her usual place for Office. At the bidding of Mother Celestine she remained seated but her voice rose true and firm in the Divine praises. "Nunc dimittis..." "Now Thou dost dismiss Thy servant, O Lord," she chanted with a heart full of longing. "Death at any moment" the doctor had said. Might she not hope that this "Nunc dimittis" would be her last?

No one was surprised at Mother's vacant place in Office that midnight. Mother Celestine had bidden her remain in bed.

Humbly, Mother Magdalen submitted but it was a precious sacrifice for her to miss the midnight office of reparation which was very dear to her apostolic heart.

God asked another little token of love from her the following morning. Though she rose at the call she found herself so weak and dizzy that she was forced to return to bed.

When the chaplain began Mass, the infirmarian who had been watching for her went to her cell in alarm. She found Mother lying quietly, absorbed in prayer, feeling no pain but very weak.

As the morning wore on the weakness continued, but she seemed in no immediate danger. Her mind was clear and alert, and though she spoke but little, she had a loving smile for each anxious face that looked in at her from the doorway.

Father Cantors visited her in the afternoon. "Did you receive Holy Communion as Viaticum, yesterday?" he asked.

"Oh yes, Father, I always do that," was her reply.

"Well, Sister, tomorrow morning I will bring Our Lord to you here in your cell."

She was appreciative. "Thank you, Father. If you do, make your intention, for I shall offer that Communion for you."

"Oh, no, no!" exclaimed the embarrassed priest, remembering the times he had deliberately withheld Communion from this humble woman. "No, Sister Magdalen, you mustn't do that, please. Offer your Holy Communion for yourself." He gave her his blessing and left, reiterating his promise for the morrow.

Just then the four o'clock bell rang for Vespers and Mother Celestine rose to go. "Yesterday at this time you were receiving Extreme Unction," she remarked. "I'm going to offer my Office for you now that God will restore your strength." Mother Magdalen smiled but did not answer. She was thinking of her "Nunc dimittis" of yesterday.

Hardly had the opening prayer of Vespers been intoned

than the infirmarian entered the choir hastily. "Come quickly," she whispered urgently to the superior, "I'm afraid Mother Magdalen is dying!"

Mother Celestine fairly flew the short distance to the foundress' cell, entered softly and sank to her knees beside the bed. Looking down at the sweet old face, lined with pain and suffering but so heavenly in its peace and serenity, she felt a pang of envy. "This is how the saints die," she thought.

"Mother," she whispered softly, wanting her to hear and yet fearful lest she be intruding on some mysterious colloquy of the soul. "Mother, are you going to leave us?"

A brief hesitation, then the foundress' head moved slightly, and she smiled. Her eyes did not open (perhaps she was already "peeking" over the threshold!) but very distinctly she said, "Just as God wills."

"Dear Mother Magdalen, will you pray for all of us, for all your daughters when you reach heaven?" persisted the superior.

Momentarily the beautiful eyes opened; the smile grew radiant. "Oh yes, indeed I will!" The promise burst from the dying lips in a rush of love and triumph.

A moment more and all was over. Catherine, the Chosen, had gone to be with God, the God Who had been so good, so very, very good to her!

IN CLOSING

One hundred years have passed since Mother Magdalen (Catherine Daemen) gave her dying promise to pray always for all her daughters.

It is no doubt due to this eternal remembrance that under the Providence of God, these daughters, the Sisters of St. Francis of Penance and Christian Charity, are found in so many parts of the world where they work for the glory of God through service to their fellowmen in hospitals, schools, nurseries, and orphanages. But Mother Magdalen's apostolic spirit which has come to her followers of each generation as a precious heritage, burns brightly in other fields which are perhaps not so well known.

In her own Netherlands, the sisters conduct schools of Household Arts, in which, through training in the domestic duties and instructions in general culture and religious principles, young girls are prepared to accept their places as wives and mothers. Home nursing is an important function in the Netherlands, and the sisters are often seen speeding along on their motorbikes to the homes of the poor and needy. Health resorts for underprivileged children are another phase of the apostolate in this country.

The United States also has a wide range of charitable labors: military academies, infant homes, retreat houses; but dearest of all, perhaps, is the work among the Negroes and the Indians.

Germany has its Studios of Religious Arts where potential artists are taught to design church windows, carve exquisite statuary and execute delicate mosaics. A very different field is the care for mentally deficient and imbecile children. The sisters care for these poor unfortunates in homes where they are protected and loved until death calls them.

Indonesia has its training centers where girls are educated to the religious life to work as teachers, nurses and social workers among their own native Javanese.

Shelters for the children of poor working parents are operated in Italy, even in the communistic areas.

In the new mission of Tanganyika, the sisters work in conjunction with the Negro Bishop and clergy to alleviate the distress and poverty of the poor Africans.

Since the free exercise of religious life is still hampered in Poland, the scope of work is narrowed and the sisters must limit themselves to care of the sick, the poor, and little children.

Educational and social works of all types are undertaken by the sisters in Brazil: Schools of Catholic Action, night classes for the education of foreigners; clinics; crèches, homes for the aged poor. Here, too, they engage in a work that demands the ultimate in sacrifice, the care of those afflicted with the dread disease—leprosy.

In the spirit of trust in the good God, these and many other services are undertaken with zeal and love, by all those, who, like Him, "chose Catherine."